Mathematics Teacher's Book

Entry 3 – Level 2

Fran Wilson, Cherry Franklin, Chris Kitching, Jamie McCulloch and Nicola Phair

Rising Stars UK Ltd.
22 Grafton Street, London W1S 4EX

www.risingstars-uk.com

Published 2009
Reprinted 2010 (twice)

Authors: Fran Wilson, Parkside Federation, Cambridge; Cherry Franklin, Chris Kitching, Jamie McCulloch and Nicola Phair, Hazel Grove High School, Stockport.
Consultant Maths Publisher: Jean Carnall
Text design and typesetting: Words & Pictures Ltd, London
Illustrator: Words & Pictures Ltd, London
Cover design: Burville-Riley Partnership

British Library Cataloguing in Publication Data.
A CIP record for this book is available from the British Library.

ISBN: 978-1-84680-632-2

Printed by Ashford Colour Press Ltd

Contents

Introduction

Achieve Functional Skills Mathematics is a series written to support the development of functional skills in Mathematics and prepares students for functional skills tests at levels 1 and 2. There are four student books in the series:

- **Entry 3 – Level 1**
  leading towards functional skills level 1

- **Level 1**
  preparation for functional skills level 1 test

- **Level 1 – Level 2**
  leading towards functional skills level 2

- **Level 2**
  preparation for functional skills level 2 test

The books can be used in sequence to build students' confidence in demonstrating functional skills gradually, or can be used independently as practice for functional skills tests.

About functional skills

Functional skills is the name given to the skills within Mathematics, English and Information Communication Technology (ICT) that have been identified by employers and educators as being necessary to enable success in further learning, employment and life.

QCA outlines that functional skills are learning tools that enable people:

- to apply their knowledge and understanding to everyday life

- to engage competently and confidently with others

- to solve problems in both familiar and unfamiliar situations

- to develop personally and professionally as positive citizens who can actively contribute to society.

  (Functional skills guidance: amplification of the standards, QCA/08/3700)

The National Curriculum and GCSE specifications have been changed to incorporate an increased focus on functional skills. GCSE examinations will include non-routine and unstructured questions that specifically focus on the functional skills content of the specification. Students will need to be familiar with the skills required to solve these sorts of questions. Schemes of work must therefore include activities that require students to develop their skills in tackling these types of problems so that they are successful in assessment and are able to function confidently beyond school and college.

Many schools and colleges offer diploma courses at Key Stages 4 and 5. Students must pass a functional skills examination in each core subject, at the level appropriate to the diploma level they are taking, to achieve a pass. Without this pass they will not gain their diploma. Familiarity with the skills they need and thorough preparation for the functional skills tests is critical to the success of these courses.

Some students may take a functional skills qualification in order to demonstrate that they have the necessary skills to use mathematics in employment and in life. It is important that all young people have the opportunity to develop their functional skills, whatever choices they make for the future.

About the Student Books

Each book is divided into five units, and each unit has a central theme running through the questions. The themes reflect common areas of functionality within the workplace, or life, and echo the contexts used by the examination bodies in assessing functional skills.

The units are further broken down into four distinct sections: A, B, C and D. Each section is self-contained and so can be used independently or, alternatively, all sections can be taken together to form a larger unit of work. This provides a flexible resource that can be incorporated easily into existing schemes of work as required.

The structure of each section is consistent throughout all the books. Information is provided about the curriculum content required for the task, as well as the area of functional skills on which to focus, particularly when working through the question itself.

Structure of the Student Books

The overall problem is sometimes broken down into questions. Each question includes information that is needed to complete it but may also require information from previous parts of the problem on the page. The style of the questions varies across the books as appropriate to the level of functional skills required.

Some pages contain hints or questions that may help students to solve the problem.

Each statement has a code that points to questions in the review exercises at the back of the book. These could be used to check confidence with the relevant mathematics before starting the problems.

The unit number and the section of the unit it covers is found at the top of the page.

Information about the mathematics that students need be confident in to successfully answer the questions is found under the title.

Each section of a unit has a suggested focus that could be used as the lesson objective.

Information can be found in text, tables, diagrams or pictures.

How to use the books

The units and problems are structured so that they can be incorporated into a scheme of work and used in a number of ways.

- **Application of curriculum content:** As each section of each unit is a self-contained problem, they can be used at the end of a topic as a real-life example. This enables students to see how the topics can be applied and appreciate the other skills that are needed to solve real-life problems. The content coverage grids (see pages 8–11) may help to identify where each sections fits into the scheme of work.

- **Regular functional skills practice:** The activities can be used on a regular basis to highlight functional skills and allow discussion about these skills as a class, so that students know how important they are in problem solving. In this model, a weekly or fortnightly lesson could be given up to solving one of the unit sections so that the whole unit is completed over a month or half-term period. The emphasis would move from matching the content to developing skills, and the area of focus identified in each unit section could be used as a basis for discussion. These process skills are found in both the National Curriculum and the Functional skills standards so are a useful way of integrating both in the curriculum.

- **'Special' activities:** In this model, each unit could be taken as a project and used in its entirety to develop students' awareness of real-life mathematics. This project period could be enriched by research into the context of the problem. This could provide opportunities for cross-curricular activities or involve contact with other parties, such as the careers service or local businesses.

- **Examination preparation:** As the units model the style of problems used by the main examination bodies, they are well suited to provide practice in the period before an external assessment. Planning regular lessons around the units in the months prior to an assessment period or before the GCSE examination would work well.

- **Formative assessment:** The units in the books achieve all of the criteria outlined in the QCA document on assessing functional skills (Qualifications criteria for functional skills Qualification, QCA/09/4269) by setting realistic problems that require understanding of the context and providing opportunities to demonstrate problem-solving skills. This makes the units suitable for use as formative assessment activities that focus on functionality. This would inform students and their teachers/trainers about their progress in problem solving and allow for appropriate measures to be taken to support further progress. Photocopiable student self assessment sheets can be found on pages 58–63.

- **Curriculum content assessment:** Each unit is matched to particular areas of the curriculum and can be used for assessment in conjunction with the Assessing Pupils' Progress assessment criteria from the National Strategies.

The review exercises included at the end of each Student Book cover the mathematical content required to work through the units. The questions demonstrate the level of competence needed to work through the problems and may be used to start the unit, allowing teachers to check that students are confident in these skills. They could also provide a self-assessment opportunity for students who are working independently on the units. Either use would enable students to create targets for revision, prior to undertaking the unit.

Progression through the functional skills levels

Functionality will allow individuals to apply their knowledge with confidence in familiar or unfamiliar situations. This will allow them to develop a method to solve any problem they meet, even if they do not know how to do so beforehand, and then communicate the solution clearly to others. Thus, the individual will become an independent learner and be able to work effectively in the workplace. However, there is a significant difference in the style of problem that would be achievable for someone working at functional skills entry level to someone who is functioning at level 2.

In determining the level of a problem, QCA have indentified four areas that need to be considered: Familiarity, Independence, Complexity and Technical demand. These highlight key features of real-life problems and situations that need to be developed to ensure functionality. The units in the series reflect these developments as follows:

Familiarity: The first stage of developing functionality is to move from the familiar to the unfamiliar. At entry 3 and level 1, most problems will be similar to those seen previously and thus the transference of skills is more straightforward. As a result, the problems used in the Entry 3 – Level 1 and Level 1 Student Books are similar to those used in textbooks currently being used or content practice. At level 2, students are expected o move into less familiar or unfamiliar situations that ombine skills that may not have been used together reviously. Therefore the problems used in the evel 1 – Level 2 and Level 2 Student Books are more omplex and, although they may seem similar to ontexts used in other texts, they develop in unusual vays that use mathematics creatively.

independence: As functionality increases, the ability or the individual to work independently needs to evelop in order for their problem-solving skills o develop. This is reflected in the books so that roblems in the Entry 3 – Level 1 Student Book are uite simplistic, with single or two step problems hat can be easily indentified. However by level 2 he problems require quite complex structuring, nd planning is needed to solve them. Students re required to show a confident approach in electing and applying their mathematical skills to e successful.

Complexity: A deliberate range of styles is used cross the series to support development of omplexity. At lower levels of functionality, problems re short or are broken down into stages. As a result, heir solution requires little planning or identification f method other than selecting the appropriate nathematical method. Appropriately in the books eading towards and at level 1, the questions are pecific and highlight the key information needed. he methods used are obvious and familiar. The roblems have several stages but the questions rovide structure through the solution of the roblem, modelling the process needed in more omplex problems.

At higher levels of functionality, problems have no tructure and their solution requires the identification f important information. A successful approach eeds to be planned with appropriate methods dentified and applied efficiently. By level 2, each init contains the same phases as the previous books o continue modelling the process, but each unit nds with an unstructured problem at this level of unctionality.

Technical demand: The range of demand needed t different levels of functionality applies both o the mathematical content and the analytical equirement. The content is mapped to the existing rogramme by QCA as shown in the following table.

The series develops process skills so each book targets a particular National Curriculum level and supports content development as shown below. Some questions may draw on content from other levels as appropriate.

Entry 3 – Level 1	NC Level 3
Level 1	NC Level 4
Level 1 – Level 2	NC Level 5
Level 2	NC Level 6

Analytical demand progresses from entry 3, where students need to interpret and communicate results, to level 1 where these results need to be considered for their appropriateness and the methods used explained. To support this, the questions in the books become more analytical and those in the later books require solutions to be explained and then justified. At level 2, the students are expected to consider the accuracy of solutions and draw conclusions from the findings. The questions in the Level 1–2 and Level 2 Student Books reflect this.

Functional skills	National Curriculum	Adult numeracy	Application of number
Entry 3	Levels 1 – 3	Entry 3	
Level 1	Levels 1 – 4	Level 1	Level 1
Level 2	Levels 1 – 6	Level 2	Level 2

(Functional skills guidance: amplification of the standards, QCA/08/3700)

Functional skills criteria for mathematics

Entry 3 – Level 1

This book focuses on functional skills at entry 3 to level 1. The chart shows coverage of areas working towards level 1 mapped against the Skills standards and Coverage and range from the *Functional skills criteria for mathematics, Level 1 (QCA)*.

Skill standards	Phones A	B	C	D	Cycling A	B	C	D	Hazelnut School A	B	C	D	Youth club A	B	C	D	Walking trip A	B	C	D
Representing Understand practical problems in familiar and unfamiliar contexts and situations, some of which are non-routine							✓				✓		✓							✓
Identify and obtain necessary information to tackle the problem				✓						✓										
Select mathematics in an organised way to find solutions	✓				✓				✓						✓		✓			
Analysing Apply mathematics in an organised way to find solutions to straightforward practical problems for different purposes							✓				✓		✓						✓	✓
Use appropriate checking procedures at each stage		✓				✓				✓						✓	✓			
Interpreting Interpret and communicate solutions to practical problems, drawing simple conclusions and giving explanations			✓					✓					✓						✓	
Coverage and range (indicative)																				
Understand and use whole numbers and recognise negative numbers in practical contexts					✓	✓				✓	✓				✓					
Add, subtract, multiply and divide whole numbers using a range of strategies	✓			✓		✓				✓					✓				✓	
Understand and use equivalencies between common fractions, decimals and percentages																				
Add and subtract decimals up to two decimal places							✓		✓	✓		✓				✓	✓	✓	✓	✓
Solve simple problems involving ratio, where one number is a multiple of the other											✓									
Use simple formulae expressed in words for one- or two-step operations										✓	✓									✓
Solve problems requiring calculation, with common measures, including money, time, length, weight, capacity and temperature			✓		✓	✓	✓	✓	✓	✓		✓	✓		✓	✓	✓			✓
Convert units of measure in the same system									✓				✓							
Work out areas and perimeters in practical situations										✓										
Construct geometric diagrams, models and shapes														✓						
Extract and interpret information from tables, diagrams, charts and graphs		✓	✓			✓			✓	✓		✓	✓			✓	✓		✓	
Collect and record discrete data and organise and represent information in different ways										✓	✓									
Find mean and range																				
Use data to assess the likelihood of an outcome															✓				✓	✓

Level 1

This book focuses on functional skills at level 1. The chart shows coverage of each unit mapped against the Skills standards and Coverage and range from the *Functional skills criteria for mathematics, Level 1 (QCA).*

Skill standards	Holidaying in Florida A	B	C	D	Smashing smoothies A	B	C	D	At the match A	B	C	D	Catering A	B	C	D	Bedroom makeover A	B	C	D
Representing Understand practical problems in familiar and unfamiliar contexts and situations, some of which are non-routine				✓	✓		✓	✓						✓		✓				✓
Identify and obtain necessary information to tackle the problem	✓	✓			✓			✓			✓		✓					✓		
Select mathematics in an organised way to find solutions			✓			✓		✓		✓				✓						
Analysing Apply mathematics in an organised way to find solutions to straightforward practical problems for different purposes							✓		✓					✓	✓		✓			
Use appropriate checking procedures at each stage	✓					✓							✓							
Interpreting Interpret and communicate solutions to practical problems, drawing simple conclusions and giving explanations		✓		✓	✓	✓				✓				✓					✓	
Coverage and range (indicative)																				
Understand and use whole numbers and recognise negative numbers in practical contexts	✓				✓	✓					✓		✓							
Add, subtract, multiply and divide whole numbers using a range of strategies	✓		✓		✓	✓	✓			✓			✓				✓	✓	✓	✓
Understand and use equivalencies between common fractions, decimals and percentages		✓									✓			✓						
Add and subtract decimals up to two decimal places	✓		✓			✓									✓		✓		✓	✓
Solve simple problems involving ratio, where one number is a multiple of the other					✓									✓						
Use simple formulae expressed in words for one- or two-step operations											✓			✓		✓			✓	
Solve problems requiring calculation, with common measures, including money, time, length, weight, capacity and temperature	✓				✓	✓	✓	✓						✓	✓	✓	✓	✓	✓	
Convert units of measure in the same system							✓											✓		
Work out areas and perimeters in practical situations									✓					✓		✓	✓	✓		
Construct geometric diagrams, models and shapes														✓		✓	✓			✓
Extract and interpret information from tables, diagrams, charts and graphs	✓	✓	✓	✓	✓			✓					✓	✓	✓					
Collect and record discrete data and organise and represent information in different ways		✓					✓						✓							
Find mean and range		✓		✓							✓	✓		✓						
Use data to assess the likelihood of an outcome		✓						✓												

Level 1 – Level 2

This book focuses on functional skills at level 1 to level 2. The chart shows coverage of areas working towards level 2 mapped against the Skills standards and Coverage and range from the *Functional skills criteria for mathematics, Level 2 (QCA).*

Skill standards	Post Office				Spheres Ltd				Sorcerer's Battle				In the water				Flatbridge School			
	A	B	C	D	A	B	C	D	A	B	C	D	A	B	C	D	A	B	C	D
Representing Understand routine and non-routine problems in familiar and unfamiliar contexts and situations					✓				✓				✓		✓		✓			
Identify the situation or problems and identify the mathematical methods needed to solve them			✓						✓		✓		✓				✓			
Choose from a range of mathematics to find solutions					✓	✓					✓									
Analysing Apply a range of mathematics to find solutions		✓																✓		
Use appropriate checking procedures and evaluate their effectiveness at each stage			✓				✓											✓	✓	
Interpreting Interpret and communicate solutions to multistage practical problems in familiar and unfamiliar contexts and situations	✓									✓		✓	✓						✓	✓
Draw conclusions and provide mathematical justifications						✓						✓			✓					✓
Coverage and range (indicative)																				
Understand and use positive and negative numbers of any size in practical contexts						✓								✓	✓					
Carry out calculations with numbers of any size in practical contexts, to a given number of decimal places	✓					✓	✓						✓	✓			✓	✓		
Understand, use and calculate ratio and proportion, including problems involving scale	✓	✓	✓	✓					✓		✓						✓			✓
Understand and use equivalences between fractions, decimals and percentages			✓		✓		✓		✓		✓				✓		✓			
Understand and use simple formulae and equations involving one or two operations			✓						✓		✓				✓		✓			
Recognise and use 2D representations of 3D objects		✓			✓	✓												✓	✓	✓
Find area, perimeter and volume of common shapes						✓												✓	✓	✓
Use, convert and calculate using metric, and where appropriate, imperial measures		✓	✓			✓	✓		✓					✓	✓	✓			✓	
Collect and represent discrete and continuous data, using information and communication technology (ICT) where appropriate									✓						✓					
Use and interpret statistical measures, tables and diagrams, for discrete and continuous data, using ICT where appropriate.		✓			✓				✓	✓			✓	✓			✓			
Use statistical methods to investigate situations			✓						✓											
Use probability to assess the likelihood of an outcome			✓								✓									✓

Level 2

This book focuses on functional skills at level 2. The chart shows coverage of each unit mapped against the Skills standards and Coverage and range from the *Functional skills criteria for mathematics, Level 2 (QCA)*.

	City break				Managing the Supermarket				Festival				Finance for living				Building a conservatory			
Skill standards	A	B	C	D	A	B	C	D	A	B	C	D	A	B	C	D	A	B	C	D
Representing Understand routine and non-routine problems in familiar and unfamiliar contexts and situations					✓												✓			
Identify the situation or problems and identify the mathematical methods needed to solve them			✓						✓			✓	✓							✓
Choose from a range of mathematics to find solutions														✓						
Analysing Apply a range of mathematics to find solutions				✓														✓		
Use appropriate checking procedures and evaluate their effectiveness at each stage						✓				✓					✓				✓	
Interpreting Interpret and communicate solutions to multistage practical problems in familiar and unfamiliar contexts and situations	✓							✓		✓						✓				
Draw conclusions and provide mathematical justifications		✓					✓													
Coverage and range (indicative)																				
Understand and use positive and negative numbers of any size in practical contexts							✓		✓					✓						
Carry out calculations with numbers of any size in practical contexts, to a given number of decimal places	✓			✓	✓	✓	✓			✓	✓	✓	✓	✓	✓	✓		✓	✓	✓
Understand, use and calculate ratio and proportion, including problems involving scale		✓	✓	✓		✓	✓	✓		✓	✓	✓	✓	✓	✓	✓			✓	✓
Understand and use equivalences between fractions, decimals and percentages				✓		✓		✓		✓		✓	✓							✓
Understand and use simple formulae and equations involving one or two operations		✓	✓	✓			✓	✓		✓			✓		✓	✓		✓	✓	✓
Recognise and use 2D representations of 3D objects			✓	✓			✓		✓	✓	✓						✓	✓		
Find area, perimeter and volume of common shapes			✓				✓	✓	✓	✓					✓			✓		✓
Use, convert and calculate using metric, and where appropriate, imperial measures	✓	✓	✓	✓		✓	✓		✓					✓			✓	✓	✓	✓
Collect and represent discrete and continuous data, using information and communication technology (ICT) where appropriate		✓				✓	✓	✓						✓	✓				✓	
Use and interpret statistical measures, tables and diagrams, for discrete and continuous data, using ICT where appropriate.	✓				✓	✓					✓	✓		✓	✓				✓	✓
Use statistical methods to investigate situations		✓			✓	✓					✓	✓						✓	✓	✓
Use probability to assess the likelihood of an outcome		✓							✓	✓	✓	✓	✓	✓			✓			

Unit 1 – Phones

Overview

This unit is written around the familiar context of mobile phones, and encourages students to consider many aspects of acquiring and using them. The different sections cover buying the handsets, comparing tariffs, buying extras, such as screensavers and games, and looking at bills.

Key vocabulary

estimate, calculate, exactly

Objectives

Students should focus on developing different aspects of their Using and Applying mathematics skills throughout the unit.

A – L3: Select the mathematics they use in a wider range of classroom activities

B – L3: Begin to organise their work and check results

C – L3: Review their work and reasoning

D – L3: Select the mathematics they use in a wider range of classroom activities

A Selecting a phone

This section familiarises students with different specifications of mobile phones, such as talk time and battery life. The focus is on number work and calculations, and students need to select the appropriate information from tables in order to answer the questions.

Questions to consider

- *What do these words mean: megapixels, standby, insurance, memory, talk time?*
- *How can estimating costs and measurements help in making decisions?*

Answers

1 a) Phone B, 0.55 megapixels
    b) 23 g
2 a) 2 days
    b) 12 hours, $\frac{1}{2}$ a day
3 a) 63 mm
    b) 109 mm, 11 mm and 60 mm lines drawn
    c) Phone A is 7 mm longer and the same width.
4 a) Phone D, £4.89
    b) 60 minutes
    c) No; double 25 is 50 so it has more than twice the memory.
    d) £5, £3
    e) £60
    f) If she loses the phone she will want to get it replaced.
    g) She will have paid more than the cost of a new phone.

B Selecting the best deal

This section looks at different phone packages; paying monthly and pay-as-you-go. Students pick a suitable package based on current phone usage. There is plenty of opportunity for covering a range of mental calculations when estimating.

Questions to consider

- *Why estimate answers? How best can you estimate costs and measurements?*
- *Why is it important to work out current usage before picking a new deal?*
- *What are the advantages and disadvantages of pay-as-you-go and pay-monthly deals?*

Answers

1 a) 70
    b) 280
    c) 10 hours
    d) 600 minutes
    e) 3.5 hours
    f) 14 hours
2 a) Enough minutes/enough internet for his usage.
    b) Enough texts/enough minutes for his usage.
    c) £360
3 a) £6
    b) £26.25
    c) £2.50
    d) £34.75
    e) £40 (2 × £20)
    f) £5.25

C Using the new phones

This section looks at additional functionality of mobile phones, including downloads and photographs. Students have to solve numerical problems relating to ringtones, wallpapers, games and memory storage. They become increasingly aware of the cost of downloads and an additional task could involve researching these more thoroughly.

Questions to consider
- *What different functions (apps) are available on mobile phones?*
- *How many of these do you use regularly?*
- *What should you consider when deciding on the best deal?*

Answers
1. a) The whole album is cheaper; 79p × 11 is £8.69, whereas the album costs £7.99. She saves 70p.
   b) 2 albums cost £15.98 so it would be cheaper to buy the albums.
      3 albums cost £23.87 so Lara would get value for money by downloading from the website.
2. a) 3 games
   b) 50p
3. a) 12
   b) £54
4. 24
5. a) 36 MB
   b) 988 MB
   c) 494 seconds
6. a) £5.25
   b) The 4 GB card is cheaper for same amount of memory.

D Costs

This section looks at the cost of using contract phones and top-ups over a year. Students could record their phone costs over a period of time and collect their own data to check they themselves currently have the most favourable contract or tariff.

Answers
1. a)

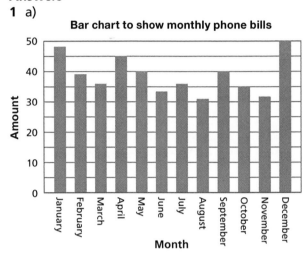

Bar chart to show monthly phone bills

   b) December
   c) August
   d) £19
   e) £465
2. a)

Top up (£)	Tally	Frequency
10	卌 卌 卌 IIII	19
20	卌 III	8
50	III	3

   b) 30 times
   c) £10
   d) £500
3. a) Lara
   b) £35

Assessment – Successful completion of this unit should provide evidence for assessment in these areas.

	NC Level 3
Using and applying mathematics	Select the mathematics they use in a wider range of classroom activities Begin to organise their work and check results Review their work and reasoning
Number	Begin to use decimal notation in contexts such as money
Calculating	Understand place value in numbers to 1000
Shape, space and measure	Add and subtract two-digit numbers mentally Add and subtract three-digit numbers using a written method Use mental recall of addition and subtraction facts to 20 in solving problems involving larger numbers
Handling data	Use standard units of time Extract and interpret information in simple lists and tables

Unit 2 – Cycling

Overview

This unit follows Javine as she progresses from bicycle novice to serious rider. There are opportunities for cross-curricular work linking with Business Studies in the scenarios involving financial decisions, and History through research into historical aspects of the Olympic Games.

Key vocabulary

range, budget, percent, quarter

Objectives

Students should focus on developing different aspects of their Using and Applying mathematics skills throughout the unit.

A – L3: Select the mathematics they use in a wider range of classroom activities

B – L3: Begin to organise their work and check results

C – L3: Try different approaches and overcome difficulties that arise when they are solving problems

D – L2: Explain why an answer is correct

A Learning the skills

This section considers the training and preparation necessary to pass the Cycling Proficiency test.

Questions to consider

- *Do you always take the cheapest option when buying something?*
- *Most people choose to use a credit or debit card to pay for things. When might you use a cheque?*

Answers

1 20 days

2 a) Bill's Bikes; £18 ÷ 2 = £9 per afternoon.
   b) £9 × 6 = £54

3 a) 180 minutes
   b) 3 hours

4 a)

Item	Cost
6 afternoons training at 'Cycle with Care'	£63.00
Highway Code book	£3.95
Helmet	£32.00
Total	**£98.95**

   b) ninety-eight pounds and ninety-five pence
   c) £115 – £98.95 = £16.05

B Buying a bike

In this section, students look at different options available from a manufacturer's listing to decide which bike would suit Javine's requirements. This involves extracting appropriate information from that provided.

Questions to consider

- *What does 'price range' mean?*
- *Why do you think a 'model number' is used?*

Answers

1 a) Nippy, Zoom, Buzz 15 and Liege 15
   b) £195
   c) £213 – £195 = £18
   d) Buzz 15, Buzz 21 and Liege 15

2 a) M4618H / Buzz 15
   b) A5223H / Liege 15

3 a) £200 – £163 = £37
   b) She should buy the Jupiter lights; Jupiter lights cost £16 ($\frac{1}{2}$ of £32) Dynamic lights cost £18 ($\frac{1}{4}$ of £24 is £6 so £6 off).

C Cycle maintenance

This section considers the costs of attending a cycle maintenance course and of cycle repairs. Students use decimal notation in the context of money and perform calculations using standard units of time.

Answers

1. a) £60 ÷ £12 = 5 weeks
   b) 7 hours
   c) 8.50 a.m.
2. a) 4.45 p.m.
   b) 20 minutes
   c) 5.45 p.m.
3. a) 7 × £1.70 = £11.90
   b) 3 × £15 = £45
   c) £15.55 + £24.70 + £26.00 + £11.90 + £45.00 = £123.15

D Training for the Olympics?

The final section of the unit looks at Javine's progress through training and her ambition to ride in the Olympic Games.

Questions to consider
- *When counting days, do you count the day that you start from?*

Answers

1. a) 3 sessions
   b) 11 sessions
   c) £62.70
   d) $16\frac{1}{2}$ hours
2. a) 54
   b) No, because half of 54 is 27 and Great Britain only won 14 medals.
   c) 54 ÷ 3 = 18
   d) 8
   e) Great Britain won about half of the cycling *Gold* Medals at the Beijing Olympics.

Assessment – Successful completion of this unit should provide evidence for assessment in these areas.	
	NC Level 3
Using and applying mathematics	Select the mathematics they use in a wider range of classroom activities Begin to organise their work and check results Try different approaches and overcome difficulties that arise when they are solving problems Review their work and reasoning
Number	Use simple fractions
Calculating	Add and subtract three-digit numbers using a written method Multiply and divide two-digit numbers by 2, 3, 4, 5, and 10 with whole number answers and remainders Use mental recall of addition and subtraction facts to 20 in solving problems involving larger numbers
Shape, space and measure	Classify 2-D shapes Use a wider range of measurements including non-standard metric units of length, capacity and mass in a range of contexts
Handling data	Extract and interpret information presented in simple tables and lists

Unit 3 – Hazelnut School

Overview

This unit looks at the planning and decision making involved in the design of a recreation area for a school. The area is to be used for a variety of activities and includes plots of various shapes and sizes for growing vegetables, a pond, and a water feature.

Key vocabulary

metre, centimetre, pattern, area, reflect, maximum, angle

Objectives

Students should focus on developing different aspects of their Using and Applying mathematics skills throughout the unit.

A – L3: Select the mathematics they use in a wider range of classroom activities

B – L3: Begin to organise their work and check results

C – L3: Use and interpret mathematical symbols and diagrams

D – L3: Try different approaches and overcome difficulties that arise when they are solving problems

A Designing the recreation area

This section looks at the cost of various items required for the recreation area by considering distances and lengths and using a simple word formula.

Questions to consider
- *Describe the features of various triangles and other polygons.*
- *Can you measure your desk to the nearest centimetre?*

Answers
1. a) 47
   b) 47 × £2 = £94
   c) 18 × £3.30 = £59.40
2. a) $11 \times \frac{1}{2} = 5.5\,m$
   b) £175 + 5.5 × £25 = £312.50
   c)

Item	Amount
2 rolls cable at £17.30 each	£34.60
5 sockets at £2.50 each	£12.50
5 back boxes at £1.50 each	£7.50
Total	**£54.60**

3. Plot 1 is a circle, Plot 2 is a parallelogram, Plot 3 is an isosceles triangle, Plot 4 is a right-angled triangle, Plot 5 is a rectangle, Plot 6 is a hexagon, Plot 7 is an octagon, Plot 8 is a rhombus.
4. a) 138 cm
   b) 1380 mm

B Growing vegetables

Students consider the arrangement of plants in the vegetable plots and the cost savings of growing vegetables for use in the school canteen.

Answers
1. a) 15
   b) 5
   c)

Row	Number of onions in the row	Total number of onions
First row	1	1
Second row	2	3
Third row	3	6
Fourth row	4	10
Fifth row	5	15
Sixth row	6	21
Seventh row	7	28
Eighth row	8	36
Ninth row	9	45
Tenth row	10	55

   d) 55 – 15 = 40
2.

Plant	Height when fully grown
Sunflower	2 m
Broad bean	0.63 m
Potato	0.4 m
Courgette	0.35 m
Carrot	0.28 m
Thyme	0.05 m

3. a) 3 × 75p = £2.25
   b) 7 × £1.17 = £8.19
   c) £2.25 + £8.19 + 8 × £0.89 + 15.5 × £0.89
      = £31.355 ≈ £31.36
4. a) 3.5 kg
   b) 3.5 × 9 = 31.5 kg
   c) 31.5 × £1.75 = £55.125 ≈ £55.13

C Planning a water feature

The plan for the recreation area also includes a pond and a water feature. Students work out the area of different shaped ponds and look at the sequence of numbers formed by the paving stones around them. The section also includes further opportunity to extract information provided in a table.

Answers

1 a) 8
   b) 10
   c) 12
   d)

Pond design	Area of water (squares)	Number of blue paving stones
A	1	8
B	2	10
C	3	12
D	4	14
E	5	16
F	6	18

   e) Numbers start at 8 and then increase by 2 each time.
2 a) 10 squares
   b) £3.30 × 18 = £59.40
   c) £8 × 6 = £48 so would save £11.40
3 a) Splash, Serenade and Waterfall
   b) Serenade, £48.95

D Designing an activity area

The final section of the unit deals with items of equipment to be installed in an activity area. Students use knowledge of reflection and measuring angles but the main focus is on calculating lengths in metres and centimetres.

Answers

1

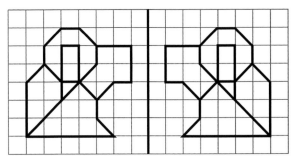

2 a) $m \approx 25°$ and $n \approx 20°$
   b) The right-hand see-saw with $n = 20°$ because this is less than 22.5°.
3 a) 5 × 30 = 150 cm = 1.5 m
   b) 1.5 + 2 = 3.5 m
4 A: 30 cm = 0.3 m, B: 60 cm = 0.6 m, C: 45 cm = 0.45 m

Assessment – Successful completion of this unit should provide evidence for assessment in these areas.	
	NC Level 3
Using and applying mathematics	Select the mathematics they use in a wider range of classroom activities Begin to organise their work and check results Use and interpret mathematical symbols and diagrams Try different approaches and overcome difficulties that arise when they are solving problems
Number	Begin to use decimal notation in contexts such as money
Calculating	Solve whole number problems including those involving multiplication or division Multiply and divide two-digit numbers by 2, 3, 4, 5, and 10 with whole number answers and remainders Use mental recall of addition and subtraction facts to 20 in solving problems involving larger numbers
Shape, space and measure	Use a wider range of measurements in a range of contexts
Handling data	Extract and interpret information presented in simple tables and lists

Unit 4 – Youth club

Overview

This unit considers responsibilities and decisions made by young people attending a youth club and by the youth leader running the club. The emphasis throughout the unit is on building confidence in number.

There is opportunity for cross-curricular links to Citizenship with a focus on team-building, fundraising and working with other people outside of school.

Key vocabulary

difference, multiple, capacity, remainder

Objectives

Students should focus on developing different aspects of their Using and Applying mathematics skills throughout the unit.

A – L3: Review their work and reasoning

B – L3: Try different approaches and overcome difficulties that arise when they are solving problems

C – L3: Select the mathematics they use in a wider range of classroom activities

D – L3: Begin to organise their work and check results

A Going to the youth club

This section explores the need for the young people to budget for activities they would like to participate in. The pool tournament provides a setting for developing understanding of simple fractions in different contexts.

Questions to consider
- *How do you save for activities you want to take part in?*
- *How many matches are played in a knock-out competition with 8 players? What about 16 players?*
- *What are the usual names for the last three rounds of a competition?*

Answers
1 a) £2
   b) 18 days (including the day of the contest)
2 a) Yes; there were three girls out of eight in total.
   b) 3 matches
   c) $\frac{1}{3}$
3 a) 15 balls
   b) $\frac{7}{15}$
   c) $\frac{8}{15}$
4 Saturday night activity. He will save from £1 to £2 depending on activity chosen.

B Preparing for the weekend away

This section looks at raising the money needed to buy equipment for a trip away, by washing cars. Students consider some of the practicalities involved when shopping for suitable camping equipment.

Answers
1 a) £8
   b) £48
   c) £48 ÷ £4 = 12 cars
2 a) £40
   b) 10 cars
3 No. He needs 500 ml of soap.
4 a) 24 litres
   b) 18 litres
5 a) He should buy the 0°C sleeping bag.
   b) The other sleeping bags cannot be used below 5°C and 10°C so will not keep him warm enough.
6 a) 47 litres
   b) No; it would take him to 62 litres.

C Running the youth club

This section considers the task of keeping records about the number of young people attending the youth club and their distribution across the activities available to them.

Answers
1. a) June 5th
   b) May 29th
   c) 136
2. £68
3. a) £32
   b) 64
4. £229
5. a) 4 groups
   b) 2
6. 7
7. 7
8. 3

D Stocking up

This section looks at the organisation of the youth club tuck shop. A report aspect is included to show that the youth club is an organisation that has to keep a record of its past and future sales. Students should understand that advance planning in all areas of an organisation is important.

Questions to consider
- *What is a healthy/unhealthy snack?*
- *Why are target figures set?*
- *What does seasonal mean?*
- *Can you think of examples where it is important to consider seasonal figures?*

Answers
1. a) cereal bars
   b) Young people often prefer chocolate, crisps and fizzy drinks to cereal bars.
2. 135 (water and cereal bars)
3. a) £283
   b) £77
4. a) £175
   b) £185
5. Not quite; 6 × £30 = £180 so he is £5 short of his target.
6. a) April
   b) December; youth club members on holiday for Christmas, less money to spend etc.
7. December, February and May
8. a) January, February and April
   b) 3 months – December, March and May
9. March

Assessment – Successful completion of this unit should provide evidence for assessment in these areas.	
	NC Level 3
Using and applying mathematics	Review their work and reasoning Try different approaches and overcome difficulties that arise when they are solving problems Select the mathematics they use in a wider range of classroom activities Begin to organise their work and check results
Number	Use simple fractions that are several parts of a whole Use decimal notation in contexts including using money
Calculating	Add and subtract three-digit numbers using a written method Multiply and divide two-digit numbers by 2, 3, 4, 5, and 10 with whole number answers and remainders Use mental recall of addition and subtraction facts to 20 in solving problems involving larger numbers Solve whole number problems including those involving multiplication or division that may give rise to remainders
Shape, space and measure	Use a wider range of measurements including non-standard metric units of length, capacity and mass in a range of contexts
Handling data	Extract and interpret information presented in simple tables, lists and bar charts

Unit 5 – Walking trip

A Train times and fares

The first section of the unit focuses on reading information about weather from charts, and train times from timetables. This section allows students to gain confidence when calculating in hours and minutes using 12- and 24-hour clock times.

Questions to consider

- Where do you often come across bar charts showing rainfall?
- What do you look for to tell when there is the least rain?

Answers

1 a) July and August
   b) August and September
   c) August
2 August; it has the lowest rainfall for all three mountains.
3 a) 07:35, 08:35 and 09:35 trains
   b) From 07:35 to 12:14 is 4 hours and 39 minutes.
4 a) none
   b) 8 minutes
   c) 5 hours 39 minutes
5 a) 11.06 p.m.
   b) 10 hours 48 minutes
   c) 5 hours 25 minutes
6 a) 11.50 + 58.10 + 104.00 + 75.00 = £248.60
   b) £248.60 × 3 = £745.80

B Buying the equipment

The focus of this section is on buying the correct walking clothes for the trip. Students find the cost of items after they have been discounted. Additionally, they convert store loyalty points into cash equivalents.

Questions to consider

- Why are 4-digit PIN numbers used with bank cards?
- What other loyalty schemes, as well as collecting points, can you think of?

Answers

1 £15.00 + £7.50 = £22.50
2 £30.00
3 a) £57.20 + £44 + £39.95 + £30 + £22.50 + £12.95 + £4.95 = £211.55
   b) £211.55 – £10 = £201.55
   c) 20 × 5 = 100 points
4 a) 2248, 2284, 4822, 4282, 4228, 8422, 8242, 8224
   b) 2248 – two thousand two hundred and forty eight
5 a) £12.08
   b) 895 points
   c) 1208 – 895 = 313
   d) £3.13

C Camping

In this section, students consider buying camping equipment and look at dimensions of various tents. Students also work out the cost of staying at different campsites; taking into consideration how the price is dependent on the days of the week you stay.

Questions to consider

- What factors do you need to consider when buying a sleeping bag? A tent?
- Why is the cost of campsites sometimes different on weekdays from weekends?

Answers

1 a)

Item	Price	Quantity	Cost
Camping stove	£34.95	1	£34.95
Cutlery	£3.49	3	£10.47
Bowls	£1.10	3	£3.30
Cups	£1.00	3	£3.00
Plates	£1.25	3	£3.75
Pan set	£24.99	1	£24.99
Sleeping bag	£25.00	3	£75.00
Tent	£69.95	1	£69.95
		Total	£225.41

  b) £225.41 ÷ 3 = £75.13666 ≈ £75.14

2 a) 1.1 m
  b) No; she is over 1.1 m tall.
  c) Yes; the length of the tent is 220 cm, which is 2.2 m and the tallest person is 1.71 m tall.

3

Campsite	Dates	Days of the week	Cost
1	3rd	Friday	£15
	4th	Saturday	£12
	5th	Sunday	£15
2	6th	Monday	£19
	7th	Tuesday	£19
	8th	Wednesday	£19
3	9th	Thursday	£9
	10th	Friday	£14
	11th	Saturday	£14
	12th	Sunday	£9
		Total cost	£145

D Climbing the peaks

This section looks at the time taken for each stage of the trip; how long it takes to reach the peak, how much rest they need before setting off again and the time they return to the base of the mountain. Students have to work out average speeds and think about changes that affect the average speed.

Questions to consider
- *Why do you work out an average speed?*
- *Why does the terrain affect the average speed?*
- *Why does the average speed change depending on whether you are going up or down the mountain?*

Answers

1 a) 2.30 p.m.
  b) 3.15 p.m.
  c) 6.15 p.m.

2 a) 1.75 km per hour
  b) 2.3 km per hour
  c) It is easier to walk downhill so they travel faster.

3 a) 3.00 p.m.
  b) 3.15 p.m.
  c) 5.15 p.m.
  d) 6 km
  e) 1.5 km per hour
  f) 3 km per hour

4 a) 7.5 km
  b) 2.30 p.m.
  c) 3.30 p.m.
  d) 5.30 p.m.
  e) 1.5 km per hour
  f) 3.75 km per hour

5 14 km + 12 km + 15 km = 41 km

Assessment – Successful completion of this unit should provide evidence for assessment in these areas.	
	NC Level 3
Using and applying mathematics	Begin to organise their work and check results Try different approaches and overcome difficulties that arise when they are solving problems Review their work and reasoning Select the mathematics they use in a wider range of classroom activities
Number	Begin to use decimal notation in contexts such as money
Calculating	Add and subtract two-digit numbers mentally Add and subtract three-digit numbers using a written method
Shape, space and measure	Use standard units of time
Handling data	Extract and interpret information presented in simple tables, lists and bar charts

Unit 1 – Holidaying in Florida

Overview

This unit covers the many skills needed to organise a holiday. Activities range from booking flights, looking at weather conditions, currency conversions and planning a visit to a theme park.

The unit could be used as a cross-curricular link with Geography, looking at where people go on holiday and why they choose certain locations.

Key vocabulary

conversion, denomination

Objectives

Students should focus on developing different aspects of their Using and Applying mathematics skills throughout the unit.

A – L4: Develop own strategies for solving problems

B – L4: Present information and results in a clear and organised way.

C – L4: Present information and results in a clear and organised way.

D – L4: Use their own strategies within mathematics and in applying mathematics to practical situations

A Planning a package

The first section addresses the total cost of going on holiday, including flights with in-flight meals, and accommodation. Students extract the information they need from tables and use their number skills to work out holiday prices. Calculators are not needed but may be useful for some students.

Questions to consider
- *Why do you think the prices of flights and hotels vary depending on the month?*
- *Why do you think there is such a big difference in prices at different hotels?*

Answers
1 a) £370
   b) £185
   c) $\frac{1}{2}$
   d) (£370 + £185) × 2 = £1110
2 £8 × 4 = £32
3 a) 4 × £6 = £24
   b) £24 × 2 = £48
4 a) £56 + £32 + £48 = £136
   b) £1110 + £136 = £1246
5 a) £85
   b) £85 × 4 = £340
   c) £340 × 7 = £2380
6 a) £35
   b) £35 × 4 = £140
   c) £140 × 7 = £980
7 £980 + £2380 = £3360
8 £1246 + £3360 = £4606

B Orlando weather

This section focuses on students reading and interpreting weather information from a variety of tables and graphs.

Questions to consider
- *How can you calculate the range? What does it show?*
- *What are maximum and minimum temperatures? When might they occur during the course of a day?*
- *How can you use previous data to estimate probability?*

Answers
1 a)

Month	Rainfall (mm)
May	90
June	200
July	180
August	170
September	150

   b) June   c) May   d) 110 mm
2 a) July   b) May   c) May
3 a) September
   b) May
   c) $\frac{2}{10} = \frac{1}{5}$
   d) September; $\frac{5}{10}$ is equivalent to 50%
   e) $\frac{1}{2}$ is equivalent to 50% so both reports are saying the same thing

C Changing currency

This section covers changing money into another currency and using a conversion graph to compare prices in different currencies.

Questions to consider
- *What different denominations can you split pounds (£) into?*
- *Are conversion rates between currencies always the same?*

Answers

1 a) Examples of some possible combinations are:

$1	$5	$10	$20
50	0	0	0
0	10	0	0
5	1	4	0
0	0	1	2

b) 1 × $10 with 2 × $20

2 a) £5
b) £3
c) £14
d) £4
e) £16

3

Item	UK price (£)	US price (£)	Difference
Mickey Mouse Toy	£8.00	£5.00	£3.00
Donald Duck pencil	£2.00	£3.00	−£1.00
Goofy mug	£5.00	£4.00	£1.00
Minnie Mouse lamp	£14.00	£14.00	£0.00
Fantasia DVD	£18.00	£16.00	£2.00

4 £5 + £2 + £4 + £14 + £16 = £41

D Scream Towers

The final section of the unit looks at financial aspects of the decision-making process in planning a visit to a theme park. Students calculate the mean amounts spent in the park and draw conclusions based on the range and the mean.

Answers

1 a) $6
b) $60
c) $51
d) $40
e) 10-day Lounging Lizard
f) $240
g) People spend money on extras when in the theme park so management can charge less. Also entices people to stay for longer.

2 a)

Item	Price	Quantity	Cost
Baseball cap	$2.50	2	**$5.00**
Key ring	$1.25	5	**$6.25**
Lunch box	$4.75	3	**$14.25**
Pencil	$0.20	18	$3.60
Total cost of order			**$29.10**

b) $0.90

3 a) $24
b) $260
c) $26 per day
d) Sarah was probably right; the amounts have a large range, they spent up to $13 more than the average or up to $11 less than the average every day.

Assessment – Successful completion of this unit should provide evidence for assessment in these areas.

	NC Level 3	NC Level 4
Using and applying mathematics	Develop own strategies for solving problems Present information and results in a clear and organised way. Use their own strategies within mathematics and in applying mathematics to practical situations	
Number	Begin to use decimal notation in contexts such as money	Use place value to multiply and divide whole numbers by 10 or 100 Recognise approximate proportions of a whole and use simple fractions, decimals and percentages to describe them
Calculating	Add and subtract three-digit numbers using a written method	Solve problems with or without a calculator
Handling data	Extract and interpret information presented in simple tables, lists and bar charts	Understand and use the mean and range to describe sets of data Construct and interpret frequency diagrams and simple line graphs

Unit 2 – Smashing smoothies

Overview

This unit covers number and measurement skills involved in making smoothies, from buying the ingredients to working out recipes for different numbers of people as well as comparing data on different people's favourite flavour.

There are opportunities for linking with Food Technology through discussions about the nutritional value of different smoothies, as well as developing the concept of ratio in a practical way.

Key vocabulary

proportion, ratio, estimate, calculate exactly

Objectives

Students should focus on developing different aspects of their Using and Applying mathematics skills throughout the unit.

A – L4: Search for a solution by trying out ideas of their own

B – L4: Use their own strategies within mathematics and in applying mathematics to practical situations

C – L4: Develop own strategies for solving problems

D – L4: Present information and results in a clear and organised way

A Re-writing recipes

This section focuses on working with the different units involved in recipes. The questions are straightforward and require efficient mental calculations.

Questions to consider

- What is a smoothie?
- What are considered healthy ingredients?
- Which type of smoothie ingredients are measured in grams and which in millilitres?

Answers

1 a) 150 g
   b) 225 ml
   c) 150 g
   d) The Wide Awake smoothie because it contains only fruit and fruit juice.
   e) The Chocotastic smoothie because it contains chocolate spread.
2 a) 400 ml milk, 100 g chocolate spread, 200 g banana, 2 tbsp vanilla ice-cream.
   b) 525 ml cranberry juice, 1050 ml orange juice, 700 g melon, juice of seven lemons.
   c) 10
   d) 4
   e) 3 : 2 : 1
3 a) Two portions: the melon is one portion and the fruit juice is another (fruit juice can only be counted as one portion).
   b) Because one portion of fruit has to be at least 70 g.
   c) One portion: the smoothie includes 100 g of banana.

B The price is right

This section develops mental calculation skills involved in buying the ingredients. Students should use estimates to check their answers are reasonable.

Questions to consider

- Why is it useful to make estimates in a supermarket?
- Are multipacks always cheaper than buying items singly?

Answers

1 a) 3
   b) £6
2 a) 3
   b) £12
   c) £11.61
   d) 100 g
3 a) 72p
   b) 50 g
4 a) 2
   b) £2
   c) £1.96
   d) 500 g
5 a) £23.17
   b) £20 and £10
   c) £6.83
6 a) £1.60
   b) One Exotic smoothie is £1.55. One Yummy smoothie is £1.65. So it is cheapest to buy the Exotic smoothie multipack as the cost for one smoothie is the lowest.

C Units and measuring

The focus of this section is on reading scales and converting between standard units of mass and capacity.

Answers

1. a) 350 g
   b) 50 g
2. a) 320 g
   b) 120 g
3. a) 400 ml
   b) 400 ml
4. a) 1.5 kg
   b) 1950 g
   c) 130 g
   d) 2 cartons
   e) yes; 375 ml

D Which smoothie is best?

This section looks at different ways of displaying data and interpreting results.

Questions to consider

- *Who might be interested to know the results of a survey on favourite smoothie flavours?*

Answers

1. a)

Smoothie	Tally	Frequency
Wide Awake	IIII II	7
Chocotastic	IIII IIII	10
Forest Feast	III	3

b)

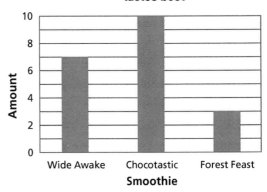

Bar chart to show which smoothie tastes best

c) 20
d) Chocotastic
e) Forest Feast
f) 3

2. a) Wide Awake
   b) Chocotastic
   c) 15

3. Any sensible answers comparing the two sets of results, e.g. Atiq's family preferred the Wide Awake smoothie, whereas his friends preferred the Chocotastic smoothie.

4. a) It is the largest section of the pie chart and passionfruit smoothies had the most number of votes.
   b) Mango and banana are sections E or B as these two smoothies have an equal number of votes. Strawberry is section D as it has fewer votes than mango and banana. Kiwi is section C as it has the fewest votes.

Assessment – Successful completion of this unit should provide evidence for assessment in these areas.

	NC Level 3	NC Level 4
Using and applying mathematics	Use and interpret mathematical symbols and diagrams Review their work and reasoning	Search for a solution by trying out ideas of their own Use their own strategies within mathematics and in applying mathematics to practical situations Present information and results in a clear and organised way
Number	Begin to use decimal notation in contexts such as money	Begin to understand simple ratios
Calculating		Use a range of mental methods of computation with all operations Use efficient methods of addition and subtraction and short division and multiplication Solve problems with or without a calculator
Shape, space and measure	Use a wide range of measures including non standard units and standard metric units of length, capacity and mass in a range of contexts	Choose and use appropriate units and instruments Interpret, with appropriate accuracy, numbers on a range of measuring instruments
Handling data	Extract and interpret information presented in simple tables, lists, bar charts and pictograms	Record discrete data. Construct and interpret frequency diagrams

Unit 3 – At the match

Overview

This unit considers situations related to a football match and looks at the match day from a different person's point of view. Students need to calculate lengths and perimeters of the pitch, distances to matches, costs, income and profit from refreshments, and player ratings.

Key vocabulary

area, perimeter, volume, mean, range, estimate

Objectives

Students should focus on developing different aspects of their Using and Applying mathematics skills throughout the unit.

A – L4: Develop own strategies for solving problems

B – L4: Use their own strategies within mathematics and in applying mathematics to practical situations

C – L4: Present information and results in a clear and organised way

D – L4: Search for a solution by trying ideas of their own

Ⓐ Groundsman

Areas and perimeters are used in the context of the pitch and the amount of paint needed to paint the lines is calculated.

Questions to consider

- *What is the smallest/largest size a football pitch can be?*
- *What shape could a football pitch be?*

Answers

1 a) 7
  b) 3
2 a) 10,800 m²
  b) 420 m
  c) 9 containers
3 a) 1500 cm³
  b) 50 containers
4 a) 60 m by 45 m
  b) 630 m
  c) 370 m

Ⓑ The fan

This section focuses on extracting information from tables and lists as well as calculating distances, times and the cost of buying refreshments. Familiarity with planning a journey will be relevant to most students; here they are asked to consider time management as well as the distances travelled.

Questions to consider

- *Where else do you see 'Meal Deals' and are they much cheaper than individual purchases?*

Answers

1 a) 65 km
  b) 121 km
2 342 km to Portsmouth
3 14 km to Manchester
4 11.30 a.m.
5 a) 1.33 p.m.
  b) 1.48 p.m.
6 a) 8
  b) 4
  c) 5
7 a) £3.95
  b) £3.10
  c) £2.50
8 £0.35
9 3.05 p.m.

C Kiosk manager

This section looks at factors to be considered when planning how much stock to order. This leads students on to calculating percentages and fractions of amounts. Students use simple word formulae to work out the profit made on sales and should realise the importance of estimations, particularly with large numbers.

Questions to consider
- *Why is it necessary to estimate?*
- *Is the average attendance over several football matches likely to be exactly accurate?*
- *What is meant by the income of a business?*
- *What do you need to know, apart from income, to work out profit?*

Answers
1 a)

Opposition	Attendance	To the nearest 1000
Manchester City	20,035	20,000
Fulham	20,928	21,000
Arsenal	26,196	26,000
Liverpool	29,578	30,000
Manchester	27,264	27,000

b) 30,000 27,000 26,000 21,000 20,000
c) 10,000
d) 9543
2 24,800
3 50% tea, 25% meat pies, 10% chocolate bars
4 a) tea
  b) coffee
5 a) £77
  b) £121
  c) £44

D Team manager

This section focuses on the use of negative numbers and averages. Simple calculations with negative numbers are required; this work can be extended if necessary. Consideration can be given to calculating the mean 'stamina' etc. of players.

Questions to consider
- *What other uses of negative numbers are there?*
- *How can you work out a team's goal difference?*

Answers
1 a) Tottenham and Stoke City
  b) 3
  c) 7
2 a)

Match			Win, lose or draw	Goal difference
Hazel Grove United	0–2	Tottenham Hotspur	L	–2
Hazel Grove United	4–3	Blackburn Rovers	W	+1
Hazel Grove United	1–1	Fulham	D	0
Hazel Grove United	2–4	Manchester United	L	–2
Hazel Grove United	0–5	Arsenal	L	–5
Total goal difference after 5 games				–8

b) 4 points
3 a) Thomas = 34, Jenkins = 33, Latz = 30
  b) Thomas = 6.8, Jenkins = 6.6, Latz = 6
  c) Thomas = 5, Jenkins = 4, Latz = 3
  d) Possible answer could be: Thomas; he has the highest mean rating.

Assessment – Successful completion of this unit should provide evidence for assessment in these areas.

	NC Level 3	NC Level 4
Using and applying mathematics	Try different approaches and find ways of overcoming difficulties that arise when they are solving problems	Develop own strategies for solving problems. Use their own strategies within mathematics and in applying mathematics to practical situations. Present information and results in a clear and organised way. Search for a solution by trying out ideas of their own
Number/Algebra	Recognise negative numbers in contexts such as temperature	Begin to use simple formulae expressed in words. Recognise approximate proportions of a whole and use simple fractions and percentages to describe these
Calculating	Add and subtract three-digit numbers using a written method	Use efficient methods of addition and subtraction and short multiplication and division
Shape, space and measure	Use standard units of time	Find perimeters of simple shapes and areas by counting squares
Handling data	Extract and interpret information presented in simple tables, lists, bar charts and pictograms	Understand and use the mode and range to describe sets of data

Unit 4 – Catering

Overview

This unit looks at setting up a catering business, from the initial market research and finding suitable company premises, through to the selection and costing of a menu and finally onto developing the public image of the company by designing and costing a suitable logo.

Key vocabulary

range, mean, area, perimeter, reflection, symmetry

Objectives

Students should focus on developing different aspects of their Using and Applying mathematics skills throughout the unit.

A – L4: Present information and results in a clear and organised way

B – L4: Develop own strategies for solving problems

C – L4: Use their own strategies within mathematics and in applying mathematics to practical situations

D – L4: Search for a solution by trying out ideas of their own

A Market research

This unit focuses on market research, emphasising the importance of testing and evaluating the potential market before committing to a business investment.

Questions to consider
- *What would it be important to find out before starting a catering business or a restaurant?*

Answers
1 a) 10
   b) tuna salad
   c) It means that the majority of people thought that the food was unhealthy.
   d) The four foods with the highest total score are: tuna salad (43), lasagne (36) cheeseburger (31) and pizza (31). These are the foods that the majority of people thought were the healthiest. Ronaldo would need to decide whether their assumptions were correct.

2 a)

Maximum spend on a meal?				
Up to £5	£6–£10	£11–£15	£16–£20	Over £20
	ⵌ I	ⵌ	III	I

   b) Everyone would be willing to pay his prices.

3 a)

Favourite foods		
Food	Tally	Frequency
$\frac{1}{4}$ lb flame-grilled cheeseburger	ⵌ ⵌ ⵌ ⵌ ⵌ ⵌ II	32
Chips & gravy from the chippie	ⵌ ⵌ ⵌ III	18
Cheese & tomato pizza	ⵌ ⵌ ⵌ ⵌ ⵌ IIII	29
Lasagne	ⵌ ⵌ ⵌ ⵌ ⵌ	25
Home grilled fish fingers	ⵌ ⵌ ⵌ III	18
Tuna salad with olive oil dressing	ⵌ III	8
	Total	130

   b) tuna salad
   c) Cheeseburger, pizza and lasagne. They have the highest frequency.
   d) Tuna salad was not very popular. Although people think it is healthy, most people wouldn't buy it.

B The company premises

This section looks at choosing between various options of building size. Students need to calculate area and perimeter and also draw simple scale drawings. Students work out costs using a simple word formula.

Answers
1 a) Option 1 = 36 m², option 2 = 45 m², option 3 = 42 m², option 4 = 36 m², option 5 = 45 m².
   b) He should choose option 3 because at 42 m² this is closest to 40 m².

2 a)

Real size	1 m	2 m	3 m	4 m	5 m	6 m	7 m
Size on drawing	2 cm	4 cm	6 cm	8 cm	10 cm	12 cm	14 cm

b) Scale drawing should be
14 cm width × 12 cm height.
c) Food preparation table = 8 m², large
fridge = 6 m² and storage cupboard
= 5 m². Total area is 19 m².
d) 42 m² – 19 m² = 23 m²
e) £550
3 a) 26 m
b) £165

C Food and nutrition

This section deals with evaluating competitors'
menus before planning your own. This involves
comparing information from displays. The
section also includes a short logic problem.

Questions to consider
- *What else apart from competitors' prices
  might you want to consider when opening a
  restaurant?*

Answers
1 a) Sea-licious Squid Rings   £3.95
    Perfect Pepperoni Pizza   £2.95
    Terrific Tuna Salad   £2.45
    Vibrant Veggie Burger   £2.45
    Fearsome French Fries   £1.80
    Garlic Bread   £1.10
b) £14.70 ÷ 6 = £2.45
c) Posh Nosh = £30 ÷ 6 = £5.
    Difference = £5 – £2.45 = £2.55
d) 8 × £2.45 = £19.60
e) Minimum order of 10 means 8 orders
    cost £54.
2 a) £2.55
b) £1.10
3 Card A: Belting Burger, Card B: Penalty Pizza,
Card C: Long-ball Lasagne.

D Public image of the company

The last section of the unit involves using
symmetry to help design a logo, area
calculations and a simple formula to
calculate costs.

Questions to consider
- *Which vehicles sometimes display words
  written backwards?*

Answers
1

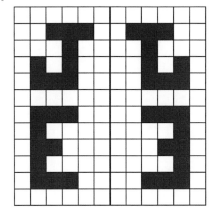

2 a) 9 cm²
b) 19 cm²
3 19 × £4.95 + £45 = £139.05
4 a)

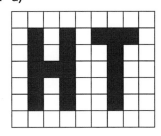

b) 18 cm²
c) £134.10
d) HT is cheaper. £139.05 – £134.10 = £4.95

Assessment – Successful completion of this unit should provide evidence for assessment in these areas.	
NC Level 4	
Using and applying mathematics	Present information and results in a clear and organised way Develop own strategies for solving problems Use their own strategies within mathematics and in applying mathematics to practical situations Search for a solution by trying out ideas of their own
Number/Algebra	Order decimals to three decimal places Begin to understand simple ratios Begin to use simple formulae expressed in words
Calculating	Multiply a simple decimal by a single digit
Shape, space and measure	Reflect simple shapes in a mirror line, translate shapes horizontally or vertically Find perimeters of simple shapes and areas by counting squares
Handling data	Collect and record discrete data Group data, where appropriate, in equal class intervals Construct and interpret frequency diagrams Understand and use mode and range to describe sets of data

Unit 5 – Bedroom makeover

Overview

This unit covers the many skills involved in organising a makeover of a teenager's bedroom, including buying furniture on a budget, buying a carpet and designing pictures for the walls.

Key vocabulary

estimate, reduce, calculate, scale, surface area, polygon, symmetrical, parallel, horizontal, vertical, reflection

Objectives

Students should focus on developing different aspects of their Using and Applying mathematics skills throughout the unit.

A – L4: Use their own strategies within mathematics and in applying mathematics to practical situations

B – L4: Search for a solution by trying out ideas of their own

C – L4: Use their own strategies within mathematics and in applying mathematics to practical situations

D – L4: Present information and results in a clear and organised way

A Choosing furniture

Students give estimates and calculate the actual costs of buying certain items of furniture for the bedroom.

Questions to consider
- *What do you consider to be essential items of furniture for a bedroom?*

Answers
1. a) bed frame = £100, mattress = £200, wardrobe = £300, chest of drawers = £150, television = £350, computer table = £100, iPod docking station = £200, total estimated cost = £1400
   b) total spent £1384.75
   c) £2000 – 1384.75 = £615.25
2. a) 50% of £159 = £79.50
   b) total spent £1384.75 + £79.50 + £195 = £1659.25
3. a) mini fridge £40 + Laptop £300 = £340
   b) total £343.99
   c) total £1659.25 + £343.99 = £2003.24 over spend £3.24
4. fridge (£44.99), lamp (£79.50), computer table (£99), bed frame (£116), chest of drawers (£152), mattress (£186.75), chair (£195), iPod docking station (£200), wardrobe (£282), laptop (£299) and television (£349)

B Fitting in the furniture

Students draw scale diagrams and convert between metric units to work out how the furniture can fit in the room.

Questions to consider
- *Why is a scale drawing useful?*

Answers
1. a) area = 3 × 4 = 12 m²
   b) length 300 cm, width 400 cm
   c) scale drawing of a rectangle 6 cm by 8 cm
   d) area: 6 × 8 = 48 cm²
2. a) 200 cm × 100 cm   b) 100 cm × 150 cm
   c) 50 cm × 100 cm   d) 100 cm × 100 cm
3. a), b) For example:

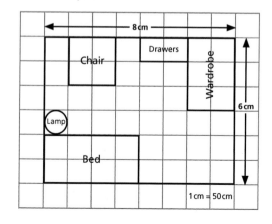

4. a) 8 cm²   b) 6 cm²   c) 2 cm²   d) 4 cm²
5. a) 20 cm²   b) 48 – 20 = 28 cm²
   c) There is plenty of floor space left.
6. For example:

7 Yes, for example:

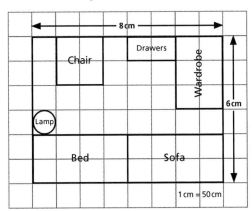

8 Yes, putting in a window/door would limit wall space and therefore what furniture can fit in.

C Painting and decorating

This section looks at the cost of carpeting the room and painting the walls. Students need to calculate the areas of rectangles to work out costs.

Questions to consider
- *Why do you need to read the whole of an advert instead of just the parts in large print?*
- *What is a call-out charge and who uses them?*

Answers
1 a) £225
   b) £305
2 a) £16
   b) £192
3 a) Smilies Carpets
   b) £305 – £192 = £113
4 3 × £160 + £50 = £530
5 a) 16 m² and 12 m²
   b) 2(16 + 12) = 56 m²
6 56 – 3 = 53 m²
7 a) 2 × £15.99 = £31.98
   b) 64 – 53 = 11 m²

D Designing pictures

The final section of the unit focuses on using symmetry and reflection to produce a design for a picture. Students decide whether the order in which they draw reflections makes a difference to the final result.

Answers
1 a) £6.99 ≈ £7 so £7 × 4 = £28
   b) £28 – £0.04 = £27.96
   c) £30 – £27.96 = £2.04
   d) 3 coins (£2, 2p, 2p)
2 a) From left to right: circle, rectangle, rhombus, kite.
   b) circle
   c) quadrilaterals
3 a), b)

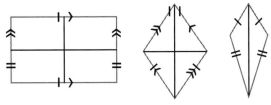

4 a)

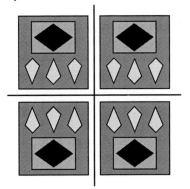

   b) No; you can reflect either way first.

Assessment – Successful completion of this unit should provide evidence for assessment in these areas.	
	NC Level 4
Using and applying mathematics	Use their own strategies within mathematics and in applying mathematics to practical situations Search for a solution by trying out ideas of their own Present information and results in a clear and organised way
Number/Algebra	Use place value to multiply and divide whole numbers by 10 or 100 Recognise approximate proportions of a whole and use simple fractions and percentages to describe these Order decimals to three decimal places
Calculating	Use efficient methods of addition and subtraction and of short multiplication and division Solve problems with or without a calculator
Shape, space and measure	Use the properties of 2-D and 3-D shapes Find perimeters of simple shapes and find areas by counting squares Choose and use appropriate units and instruments Reflect simple shapes in a mirror line

Unit 1 – Post Office

Overview

The context of the first unit will be familiar to all students. Shelley visits the Post Office to buy equipment for the new term at school. This allows some gentle calculations and reminds students that they should check receipts and change when shopping. The rest of the unit develops less familiar aspects of Post Office services: looking at passports and sending and delivering mail. Students work with measurements and realistic values throughout.

Key vocabulary

maximum, minimum, ratio, mean, average, probability

Objectives

Students should focus on developing different aspects of their Using and Applying mathematics skills throughout the unit.

A – L4: Present information and results in a clear and organised way

B – L4: Use their own strategies within mathematics and in applying mathematics to practical contexts

C – L5: Identify and obtain necessary information to carry through a task and solve mathematical problems

D – L5: Check results, considering whether these are reasonable

A Preparing for school

This introductory section uses familiar items that students need to buy for a new term and requires calculations of totals and some decision making about which is the best value. The final questions provide an opportunity for students to check their receipts and assess the accuracy of the change they are given. This provides scope for discussion on why you should do this when shopping.

Questions to consider

- *What equipment did you buy for the new term at school?*
- *Where did you buy this equipment?*
- *What other things can you do in the Post Office?*

Answers

1 a) Folding ruler; the 30 cm ruler is too long.
   b) £2.79 + £2.49 + £0.79 + £0.99 = £7.06
2 (£1.29 + £0.59 + £2.39) – £3.89 = 38p saving, using the 30 cm ruler as this is what is included in the maths set.
3 a) £4.98, £5.58, £1.99, £3.89, £0.99, £10.49
   Total = £27.92
   b) Plain paper @ £1.99 and pencil case @ £0.99.
   c) Cost of items less free items = £24.94, £30 – £24.94 = £5.06 so it was not correct.
4 a) Buying the items individually means that she would buy 10 items so would get 3 free instead of 2.
   b) Total cost (including free items) = £28.30
   Free items = 59p + 99p + £1.29 = £2.87
   Overall cost = £25.43, so she's incorrect.

B Passport

This section looks at the need to obtain passports for children and also develops awareness of measurements in familiar and unfamiliar settings. The size and cost of the photo needed for the passport may be familiar, so the questions start here. Then students will need to deconstruct the meaning of measurements within the booth to get the seat height correct to take the picture, before returning to more familiar ground to work out the cost of getting the passport quickly.

Questions to consider

- *What is a passport?*
- *When do you need a passport?*
- *Why do we need to have passports?*

Answers

1 a) 2 by 2
   b) 4 for £4 so £1 each
2 55 cm
3 15 cm
4 £46 for normal delivery or £81 to receive it within a week, so £35 extra for guaranteed delivery.

Post

This section covers the reality of postal charges and uses the dimensions set out by the Royal Mail for small letters, large letters and parcels. Students need to identify which letters fit into which category by looking at their dimensions and weights, and thus decide on the postage cost of these items. The task is structured throughout and matches the current price system at the time of publication.

Answers

1 a) 3
   b) 2
2 Four; the DL letters and the C5 letter.
3 a) 3 @ 30p = 90p
   b) As C5 letter weighs over 100 g it is classed as large letter so costs 90p.
   c) 2 × £0.90 + £0.61 + £1.24 = £3.65

D Deliveries

This part of the unit moves from services in the Post Office itself to analysing the way in which letters are delivered. It follows a post round, using the weight of the post to highlight the reality of having to deliver the post and the time it takes to complete a route. This develops students' understanding of measurements of distance and time, leading them to calculate the time that it takes to deliver letters.

Answers

1 a) 70.8 g
   b) 4
   c) 4 × 80 = 320
2 $\frac{6}{10} = \frac{3}{5}$ = 0.6 or equivalent
3 Using average, 800 × 70.8 = 56,640 g
   = 56.64 kg
4 a) 450 mm on map = 450 m in reality
   b) $\frac{450}{4500} = \frac{1}{10}$
   c) 20 mins × 10 = 200 mins = 3 hours 20 mins
5 10 + (25 + 20 + 42 + 18) + (3 × 35) + 3
   = 223 mins = 3 hours 43 mins
   6:58 + 3.43 = 10:41
   Postman returns at 10.41 a.m.

Assessment – Successful completion of this unit should provide evidence for assessment in these areas.		
	NC Level 4	**NC Level 5**
Using and applying mathematics	Use their own strategies within mathematics and in applying mathematics to practical contexts	Identify and obtain necessary information to carry through a task and solve mathematical problems
Number		Understand simple ratios
Calculating	Use efficient written methods of addition and subtraction and of short multiplication and division Check the reasonableness of results with reference to the context or size of numbers	Use known facts, place value, knowledge of operations and brackets to calculate including using all four operations with decimals to two places Apply inverse operations and approximate to check answers to problems are of the correct magnitude
Shape, space and measure	Interpret, with appropriate accuracy, numbers on a range of measuring instruments Choose and use appropriate units and instruments	Read and interpret scales on a range of measuring instruments, explaining what each labelled division represents Solve problems involving the conversion of units and make sensible estimates of a range of measures in relation to everyday situations Understand and use the probability scale from 0 to 1
Handling data		Understand and use the mean of discrete data and compare two simple distributions, using the range and one of mode, median or mean Interpret graphs and diagrams, including pie charts, and draw conclusions

Unit 2 – Spheres Ltd

Overview

This unit uses the context of a sports ball factory to develop confidence in working with fractions, negative numbers and area in unfamiliar contexts.

The unit starts by using spatial patterns – the nets of a football are a familiar design that many students will recognise. From here, the unit progresses into calculating the area and ultimately the cost of making a more unusual design – for tennis balls – and then onto looking at mass production of table-tennis balls. Finally, the context of sales gives an opportunity to use fractions in a less familiar context.

Key vocabulary

net, line symmetry, pentagon, hexagon, area, percentage wastage, difference, average, profit, revenue

Objectives

Students should focus on developing different aspects of their Using and Applying mathematics skills throughout the unit.

A – L4: Search for a solution by trying out ideas of their own

B – L4: Use their own strategies within mathematics and in applying mathematics to practical contexts

C – L5: Draw simple conclusions of their own and give an explanation of their reasoning

D – L5: Check results, considering whether these are reasonable

A Making footballs

This section introduces the factory by analysing the way in which footballs are made. The questions explore the different patterns made by the pentagons and hexagons that are used to construct a ball. Whilst the nets don't tessellate, this does give the opportunity to discuss tiling and tessellation and will be more familiar as a result. The unit finishes by asking students to visualise the net 3-dimensionally by working out whether a strategy will work.

Questions to consider
- *What is a sphere?*
- *How do you make a sphere?*
- *How are footballs made?*

Answers
1 a)

b) 5
2 a)

b) 3
c) No, 5 of the hexagon design will have 15 pentagons, which is 3 too many.
3 a) There need to be 10 of each.

b) Yes; each hexagon is attached to 1 pentagon, and they are positioned alternately so it will match.

B Tennis balls

This section looks at the manufacture of tennis balls using a new design. Students draw out the design using a pair of compasses and estimate the area. The rest of the questions look at how the square design will fit onto a roll of cloth and thus how much each ball will cost. The questions on percentage wastage are there to extend the most able and may require some discussion if they are unfamiliar with this idea.

Students will need cm² paper for the first question.

Answers
1 a) See drawing. Each circle should have a radius of 8 cm.

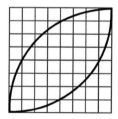

b) Each leaf has an area of 36.5 cm². Allow approximations between 33 and 40 cm².
c) For all 4 leaves, the area is 146 cm². Allow 4 × their answer to part b).
2 a) 16 cm × 16 cm
b) area = 16² = 256 cm²

3 a) 256 – their answer for Qu 1 b).
   Accurate answer is 110 cm².
b) Their answer for 3 a) ÷ 256 × 100.
   Accurate answer ≈ 43%
4 5200 ÷ 16 = 325 squares
5 a) 160 ÷ 16 = 10 squares
b) 10 × 325 = 3250 squares
6 a) 500 ÷ 3250 ≈ 15p
b) 43% of 15p = 6.45
   ≈ 6p of the cost is wasted
   Use their answer from Qu 3 b) for
   percentage wastage.

C Packing

This section uses the unusual context of packing table-tennis balls to understand the meaning of positive and negative numbers. Students calculate the standard weight of a box of 144 balls and then use the weight difference of particular boxes to answer some questions. The context of quality control is used and this may be new to students.

Questions to consider
- *Why do we need to check the quality of products made in a factory?*
- *What would you look for when checking boxes of table-tennis balls?*

Answers
1 144 × 2.5 = 360 g
2 (372.5 – 360) ÷ 2.5 = 5, so 149 balls
3 (352.5 – 360) ÷ 2.5 = –3, so 141 balls
4 a)

Box number	Weight difference	Number of balls
1	7.5 g	147
2	0 g	144
3	0 g	144
4	–2.5 g	143
5	0 g	144
6	0 g	144
7	10 g	148
8	0 g	144
9	–7.5 g	141
10	5 g	146

b) total weight difference = 12.5 g
   average weight difference =
   12.5 g ÷ 10 = 1.25 g
   So average weight = 360 g + 1.25 g = 361.25 g
c) Average number of balls per box =
   361.25 g ÷ 2.5 g = 144.5
   So 5 out of every 10 boxes have 1 extra ball.
d) 3 boxes out of 20 are underweight.
   So 15% of the boxes are underweight. As this is not more than 15% the QC Officer should not stop the production line.

D Sales

Finally, the unit focuses on the sales profit made on each product and the concept of sales targets. Students use fractions to compare the achievements of two sales people. They need to understand profit, as opposed to revenue, for these questions and it may be useful to research the price of the products on the internet so that they can appreciate that the profit is a fraction of the price.

Questions to consider
- *Why would a company set a sales target?*
- *What is a 'bonus'?*
- *What costs are there when making a football?*
- *Why might the total of individual sales targets be more than the overall company targets?*

Answers
1 a) 500 footballs for the month, so 125 per week.
b) 125 × £1.05 = £131.25
c) £131.25 × 4 = £525
d) 1000 × £4.50 = £4500
e) £525 + £4500 + £1.80 × 1200 = £7185
   Converting fractions to 100ths gives comparable values. (Note that the sum of individual sales targets can be more than company targets.)
2 a) Sarah
b) 0.2 × 100 = 20
c) $\frac{8}{10}$ so £25 extra
d) £25 as only 1 complete $\frac{1}{10}$ more
e) £25 × 2 = £50
f) Sarah only gets £25, so Ian gets the biggest bonus.

Assessment – Successful completion of this unit should provide evidence for assessment in these areas.

	NC Level 5
Using and applying mathematics	Draw simple conclusions of their own and give an explanation of their reasoning
Number	Round decimals to the nearest decimal place and order negative numbers in context Use equivalence between fractions and order fractions and decimals Reduce a fraction to its simplest form by cancelling common factors
Calculating	Use a calculator where appropriate to calculate fractions/percentages of quantities/measurements Solve simple problems involving ordering, adding, subtracting negative numbers in context
Algebra	Construct, express in symbolic form, and use simple formulae involving one or two operations
Shape, space and measure	Use a wider range of properties of 2-D and 3-D shapes and identify all the symmetries of 2-D shapes Solve problems involving the conversion of units and make sensible estimates of a range of measures in relation to everyday situations Understand and use the formula for the area of a rectangle and distinguish area from perimeter
Handling data	Ask questions, plan how to answer them and collect the data required

Unit 3 – Sorcerer's Battle

Overview

This unit is based on the use of computer games – a familiar topic for many students – in which they can work with money and numbers. Although this context may be unfamiliar to many teachers, it should allow students, particularly boys, to feel its personal relevance. The unit starts with a straightforward financial problem and then develops to looking at the time spent and scores of particular games. Finally, the online gaming context is used to allow students to make sense of data and choose the opponent that they are most likely to beat.

Key vocabulary

ratio, auction, average, range, pie chart, probability, fraction, expected number

Objectives

Students should focus on developing different aspects of their Using and Applying mathematics skills throughout the unit.

A – L4: Develop own strategies for solving problems

B – L4: Present information and results in a clear and organised way

C – L5: Identify and obtain necessary information to carry through a task and solve mathematical problems

D – L5: Draw simple conclusions of their own and give an explanation of their reasoning

Ⓐ Game on

This first section sets the scene by looking at how much it may cost to buy a new computer game. The three students buy the game from three different outlets; this matches realistic approaches by looking at internet shopping and auction websites. The aim is to decide which method of purchase provides the cheapest alternative. Students may be encouraged to consider balancing security of purchase against price. Discussions could develop to highlight the pros and cons of computer games.

Questions to consider
- *What games consoles are available?*
- *What types of games can you buy?*
- *How else can you play against other people?*

Answers
1 £38.99 × 0.9 = £35.09
2 2 mins 15 secs
3 a) £34.17 + £0.75 = £34.92
   b) £34.92 − £30.99 = £3.93
4 £36.82 + £3.00 = £39.82
5 a) (£40.50 + £3.50) × 7 ÷ 8 = £38.50
   b) BrilliantGames.com is cheapest at £36.99 (SuperGames = £38).
6 Peter at £35.09

Ⓑ What's the score?

This section looks at the three players and their times and scores giving students an opportunity to use data analysis to assess which player is better.

Answers
1 a) 1:18 + 1:52 + 2:30 + 2:06 = 7 hours 46 mins
   b) (120 + 289 + 454 + 305) ÷ 4 = 292
   c) 454 − 120 = 334
2 Pie chart with angles as shown.

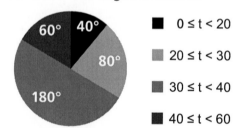

3 a) Asha has largest sector (240°) for over 30 mins, so she is slowest. Ed has more times over 30 mins than Peter, so is slower than Peter. Accept either Ed or Asha with the appropriate reasoning.
   b) Both have the fewest times over 40 mins.
   c) Ed has biggest sector for 30–40 mins, whereas this is Peter's shortest time range.
4 Peter is probably the better player as he plays the majority of his games in under 30 mins. The majority of Ed and Asha's games take over 30 mins.
5 Ed and Asha may have taken longer to complete the level by collecting more points. Ed is the best player as he has the highest number of points, and nearly double Peter's score.

C Stormy Skies

For this section, formula and ratio are used to analyse the rationale behind character development in games. The desire to win the battle fuels the decisions made when analysing different aspect of the characters.

Answers

1. a) $450 \div 10 \times 5 = 225$
   b) $450 \div 10 \times 10 = 450$
2. $10 \times (50 \div 5 + 50 \div 2 + 50 \div 10 + 50 \div 5) = 10 \times 50 = 500$, so he doesn't have enough points.
3. $10 \times (50 \div 5 + 50 \div 2 + 50 \div 10) = 400$, so 50 points left.
   $50 \div 10 \times 5 = 25$ potion-power points
4. a) 350 points
   b) Column chart as shown.

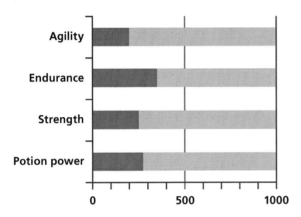

5. a) No; agility : strength is 200 : 250 which is 4 : 5, not 1 : 3.
   b) Needs 200 : 600 so needs 350 more strength points.

D Online challenge

The final section of this unit looks at internet gaming and requires students to analyse two different phases of play. First, they look at the three friends and their records against each other, and then compare these to the statistics of online players. The intention is that they rationalise their findings and use this to calculate the probability of winning against each player. This will allow them to choose the competitor who gives them the best chance of winning.

Answers

1. a) $\frac{3}{5}$
   b) $\frac{1}{3}$
   c) $\frac{3}{5} > \frac{2}{4}$ so Peter beat Ed more times than he beat Asha.
2. a) 5
   b) 9
   c) $\frac{5}{9}$
3. Peter won $\frac{5}{9}$ games, Ed won $\frac{3}{8}$ games and Asha won $\frac{4}{7}$ games. $\frac{4}{7} > \frac{5}{9}$ and $\frac{3}{8}$ so Asha is the better player.
4. $\frac{90}{120}$ or $\frac{3}{4} = 0.75$
5. $120 \div 80 \times 64 = 96$
6. Anghor has lowest probability of winning ($150 \div 240 = 0.625$) so Ed should challenge Anghor.

Assessment – Successful completion of this unit should provide evidence for assessment in these areas.		
	NC Level 4	**NC Level 5**
Using and applying mathematics	Develop own strategies for solving problems	Draw simple conclusions of their own and give an explanation of their reasoning
Number	Recognise approximate proportions of a whole and use simple fractions and percentages to describe these Begin to understand simple ratios	Reduce a fraction to its simplest form by cancelling common factors Understand simple ratios
Calculating	Multiply a simple decimal by a single digit	Solve simple problems involving ratio and direct proportion
Shape, space and measure	Choose and use appropriate units and instruments	Solve problems involving the conversion of units and make sensible estimates of a range of measures in relation to everyday situations
Handling data	Collect and record discrete data Understand and use the mode and range to describe sets of data Construct and interpret frequency diagrams and simple line graphs	Ask questions, plan how to answer them and collect the data required Understand and use the probability scale from 0 to 1 Understand and use the mean of discrete data and compare two simple distributions, using the range and one of mode, median or mean Interpret graphs and diagrams, including pie charts, and draw conclusions

Unit 4 – In the water

Overview

This unit starts with a familiar context by looking at going swimming in a leisure centre, but quickly develops into less familiar settings by exploring the temperature constraints of a swimming pool and later the pastime of scuba diving. The final section returns to a familiar context of currency exchange rates but retains the scuba diving theme so that students will need to apply what they have learnt about this sport to the problem.

Key vocabulary

average, mean, median, formula, pressure, bar, yards, feet, currency, exchange rate

Objectives

Students should focus on developing different aspects of their Using and Applying mathematics skills throughout the unit.

A – L5: Identify and obtain necessary information to carry through a task and solve mathematical problems

B – L5: Show understanding of situations by describing them mathematically using symbols, words and diagrams

C – L5: Solve word problems and investigations from a range of contexts

D – L5: Draw simple conclusions of their own and give an explanation of their reasoning

A Swimming pool

The first section of the unit looks at calculating costs and times for a family to go swimming, by extracting information from tables. Additional complexity is added by comparing the use of family tickets and loyalty cards to reduce the costs, using percentages. Finally, students need to compare the cost of regular visits to that of membership, to determine which is realistically the cheapest.

Answers

1 Tuesday, Thursday or Friday
2 £3.00 + 3 × £1.60 = £7.80
3 a) £6.50
  b) £7.80 – £6.50 = £1.30
4 65p on a family ticket
5 a) (£3.00 + £4.65) × 0.9 = £6.89 assuming that price is rounded up
  b) (£6.50 + £4.65 + 3 × £3.90) × 0.9 = £20.57 assuming that price is rounded up
6 £31.00 ÷ (£6.50 × 0.9) = £5.30. So they'll have to go at least 6 times a month.

B Weather permitting

In this section, students work with negative numbers using a relationship between outside air temperature and the water temperature of a pool. Although temperature is normally a familiar context for negative numbers, pairing this with the use of formula and the context of the swimming pool provides a less straightforward situation. Negative numbers are used in a range of different situations. When considering averages, the particular average to be used isn't specified, giving the opportunity to compare different types of

average and determine which is the most appropriate one to use.

Answers

1 –2°C
2 11°C
3 a) Monday 18th
  b) –7 + 10 = 3°C
  c) (–3 + –4 + –7 + 2 + 3) ÷ 5 + 10 = 8.2°C using the mean, or –3 + 10 = 7°C using the median. Either would be a fair average.
4 a) 22nd December
  b) 3 + 10 = 13°C
  c) 12 – 10 = 2°C, so 6 days will be too cold.
  d) $\frac{2}{8} = \frac{1}{4}$ or 0.25

C Scuba diving

The third part of the unit takes the water context into unfamiliar territory for most by looking at scuba diving. The initial questions deal with the familiar topic of calculating costs but later move on to the technical aspects of the sport by considering air pressure for the tanks needed, swimming expertise using imperial measurements, and dive and rest times. This last aspect uses simplified but accurate measures based on a dive depth of 35 feet. Rather than use the complex dive times used in the sport, the data has been provided in a format that is easier to use so students should find it manageable.

Questions to consider
- *What is scuba diving?*
- *Where might you go scuba diving?*
- *Can anyone try this sport?*
- *What equipment would you need?*

Answers

1 £150 + £60 = £210; accept £215 including the 'Have a go' session.
2 £210 + £12 × 6 = £282 or £215 + £12 × 6 = £287
3 a) 225 bars
   b) 200 yards ≈ 180 m, 180 ÷ 25 = 7.2 so she'll need to do 8 lengths.
4 Reading from graph: either 51 or 52 minutes.
5 Total dive time = $20 \times \frac{1}{4} + 15 = 20$ minutes. Reading from the graph gives a wait time of 52 minutes.
6 Reading from graph, times for each dive and wait times as in the table below.
Overall time = 3 hours 26 mins

	Dive time	Wait
Dive 1	20	52
Dive 2	15	52
Dive 3	10	27
Dive 4	10	20
Totals	55	151
	Overall total	206

D Dive holiday

In the final section of the unit, students balance prices of buying equipment against costs of hiring equipment abroad. Two well-known diving destinations are used with realistic rental costs. Students calculate the costs of buying the equipment in the first half of the questions and then calculate the rental costs in the second. They then judge whether it is better to hire or buy equipment. As most flights will carry diving gear without additional cost (provided it is within baggage allowances) these comparisons are realistic.

Answers

1 a) $\frac{2}{5}$ = 40% so is a better deal than 38% and 7%.
   b) Discount Scuba
   c) (£577.95 + £183.50 + £84) × 0.6 = £507.27
2 a) 600 × 8 ÷ 52 = £92.31
   b) Egypt: 520 EGP per day = 520 × 5 ÷ 9 = £288.89
      £288.89 + £92.31 = £381.20
   c) £507.27 – £381.20 = £126.07. It is £126.07 cheaper to hire the equipment.
3 It will cost an extra £288.89 for her holiday next year, making a total of £670.09. So Jing Wen is incorrect; it will be cheaper to buy the equipment instead of hire it.

Assessment – Successful completion of this unit should provide evidence for assessment in these areas.	
	NC Level 5
Using and applying mathematics	Show understanding of situations by describing them mathematically using symbols, words and diagrams
Number	Use understanding of place value to multiply and divide whole numbers and decimals by 10, 100 and 1000 and explain the effect Round decimals to the nearest decimal place and order negative numbers in context
Calculating	Use known facts, place value, knowledge of operations and brackets to calculate including using all four operations with decimals to two places Understand and use an appropriate non-calculator method for solving problems that involve multiplying and dividing any three digit number by any two-digit number Solve simple problems involving ordering, adding, subtracting negative numbers in context Apply inverse operations and approximate to check answers to problems are of the correct magnitude
Algebra	Construct, express in symbolic form, and use simple formulae involving one or two operations
Shape, space and measure	Read and interpret scales on a range of measuring instruments, explaining what each labelled division represents
Handling data	Interpret graphs and diagrams, including pie charts, and draw conclusions Create and interpret line graphs where the intermediate values have meaning

Unit 5 – Flatbridge School

Overview

This unit is set within the unfamiliar topic of school size and the provision of buildings. This allows familiar problems involving ratio, area and measurements to be applied within this unfamiliar context and, as a result, challenge students to apply their methods. The first section in the unit requires students to calculate the expected roll of the school and the implications of this. The unit then develops through looking at classroom size and the size of the school building and then onto creating a new block for the school. Finally, the issue of equipping a specialist suite, such as an ICT room, is used to introduce pattern.

Key vocabulary

ratio, role, projected number, area, scale, maximum, minimum, arrangement

Objectives

Students should focus on developing different aspects of their Using and Applying mathematics skills throughout the unit.

A – L5: Identify and obtain necessary information to carry through a task and solve mathematical problems

B – L5: Check results, considering whether these are reasonable

C – L5: Show understanding of situations by describing them mathematically using symbols, words and diagrams

D – L5: Draw simple conclusions of their own and give an explanation of their reasoning

A About the school

This first section explores how the number of houses in a residential area has an effect on school size. Students calculate the number of prospective young people in the school catchment area and estimate how many of these will come to the school. Using these projections they then begin to plan the effect on the number of classes in the school.

Questions to consider
- *Why does your school have the number of students that it does?*
- *Where else do students go to school?*
- *What would happen if there were 1000 more houses in your school's catchment area?*

Answers
1 $900 \times 0.2 = 180$
2 a) $180 \div 5 = 36$, so 108 in year 12 and 72 in year 13.
   b) $108 \div 900 \times 100 = 12$, $72 \div 900 \times 100 = 8$, so 12% in year 12 and 8% in year 13.
3 $(900 - 180) \div 5 = 144$
4 Years 7–11: $144 \div 32 = 4.5$, so they need five classes each. Sixth Form: $108 \div 25 = 4.32$, so 5 year 12 classes, and $72 \div 25 = 2.88$, so 3 year 13 classes.
5 $900 \div 1320 \times 100 = 68.2 \approx 68\%$
6 1340
7 a) $1340 \times 1.2 = 1608$
   b) $1608 \times 0.682 \approx 1096$ (using unrounded %)
     $1096 - 900 \approx 196$ extra students
     Allow 1093 and 193 extra students respectively for using rounded answer to Qu 5.

c) 16% students in each of years 7–11 means 175 students in each year need 6 classes. 12% students in year 12 means 132 students so need 6 classes. 8% students in year 13 means 88 students so need 4 classes.
d) One class in each year means 7 extra classes.

B How many students?

The second section of the unit focuses on classroom size and how different types of rooms require a different area. This is an integral part of school design and allows students to experience the complex decisions school management have to make. Students follow a process closely related to the actual formulas used to calculate school roll and size, leading to a calculation of how much extra building space would be needed to house the additional students proposed.

Answers
1 a) $6.2 \times 6.8 = 42.16 \approx 42\,m^2$
   b) $7.8 \times 8.9 - 8.4 \times 7.3 = 8.1\,m^2$
2 a) 19
   b) $19 \times 42.16\,m^2 = 801.04\,m^2 \approx 801\,m^2$
   c) $801\,m^2 + 5 \times 61.32\,m^2 + 5 \times 69.42\,m^2$
     $= 1454.74\,m^2 \approx 1455\,m^2$
3 a) 0.71
   b) $(1455 - 60) \times 0.71 \approx 990$ students
4 $1200 - 990 = 210$
5 $210 \div 30 = 7$ new rooms
   $7 \times 60\,m^2 + 77\,m^2 = 497\,m^2$

C The new block

This section considers two different building designs and how to fit the required classrooms into the chosen design. The choice is made simply, by looking at the relationship between perimeter and area on a very intuitive level. The method of fitting the classrooms in is also considered simply, by using scale drawing and trial and improvement. In theory, the rooms should fit easily but the logistics of actually fitting the rooms in is quite a challenge. Thus students should get an appreciation of how much area can accumulate in slim spaces when these are added together.

Answers

1 No; Design A = 580 m², Design B = 550 m²
2 Perimeter of A = 160 m, perimeter of B = 110 m so B will be cheaper.
3 scale drawing of shape B
4 a) 60 m² and 77 m² respectively
   b) 5 × 60 m² + 77 m² = 377 m², so they should fit in.
5 Five 6 by 10 classrooms and one 7 by 11 classroom plus all of the office spaces added to the scale drawing. All corridors must be at least 1 cm wide on the drawing (2 m in real life).

D The computer room

This final section of the unit considers how these could be made to fit into the 77 m² sized room. There are two layouts to consider, each providing a different pattern and relation between seats and desks. The investigation is quite structured to lead students to choosing the most appropriate layout. The different lengths of the trapezium-shaped desks adds an unfamiliar complexity.

Answers

1 a) Accurate scale drawing of the desk.
   b) 6.1 cm on scale drawing = 61 cm in real life
2 a) Scale drawing made by adding desks onto each other, requiring the measurement of angles. Students may make a template to draw around.
   b) 10 desks
   c) 32.4 cm at widest point = 3.24 m in real life
   d) Need 3 polygon desk arrangements, which would fit in the space.

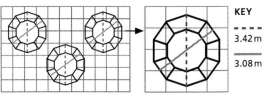

KEY
---- 3.42 m
——— 3.08 m

3 a) 1.61 m along one edge but 1.805 m when allowing for the overhang so ≈ 1.81 m
   b) Longest edge is 2 × 1 m + 0.61 m = 2.61 m
   c) Each desk adds 0.805 m in length (half of 1.61 m). So the overall length is 1 + 0.805 × (number of desks – 1).
   d) 1 + 0.805 × (13 – 1) = 10.66 m which would fit along the longest edge but there would be little space to move around the edges.
   e) Students to choose arrangement of desks – must fit in 30 desks allowing appropriate room between desks. An example of a successful layout is:

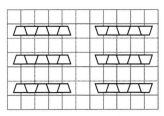

4 a) Yes, the diagram students draw should show that 30 desks will fit in.
   b) Students to choose one of the designs and give a rationale for their choice. The second arrangement has more practical use of the space as the first design has dead space in the centre of the desks, but allow any answer if the rationale makes sense.

Assessment – Successful completion of this unit should provide evidence for assessment in these areas.

	NC Level 5
Using and applying mathematics	Show understanding of situations by describing them mathematically using symbols, words and diagrams
Number	Understand simple ratio Use a calculator where appropriate to calculate fractions/percentages of quantities/measurements Understand and use an appropriate non-calculator method for solving problems that involve multiplying and dividing any three digit number by any two-digit number
Calculating	Construct, express in symbolic form, and use simple formulae involving one or two operations
Shape, space and measure	Use a wider range of properties of 2-D and 3-D shapes and identify all the symmetries of 2-D shapes Measure and draw angles to the nearest degree, when constructing models and drawing or using shapes Solve problems involving the conversion of units and make sensible estimates of a range of measures in relation to everyday situations Understand and use the formula for the area of a rectangle and distinguish area from perimeter
Handling data	Create and interpret line graphs where the intermediate values have meaning

Unit 1 – City break

Overview

This unit covers the organisation and costing of various aspects of a short stay in Edinburgh, during a festival. Students decide on the dates of key events that affect when they visit and discover the intricacies of travelling by train from one place to another, via London. They compare a small range of accommodation choices using a number of variables and then calculate the cost of making a complex souvenir, the traditional kilt.

Throughout the unit, students are expected to use a calculator and have access to measuring equipment.

Key vocabulary

scale, speed, distance, ratio, multiplier, VAT, conversion

Objectives

Students should focus on developing different aspects of their Using and Applying mathematics skills throughout the unit.

A – L6: Interpret, discuss and synthesise information presented in a variety of mathematical forms

B – L5: Draw simple conclusions of their own and give an explanation of their reasoning

C – L5: Identify and obtain necessary information to carry through a task and solve mathematical problems

D – L6: Give solutions to an appropriate degree of accuracy

Ⓐ Before you go

This section focuses on the timing of a trip away, the cost of tickets for two festival events and attending the Edinburgh Military Tattoo. Students work out when to go to each event, allowing for the availability of tickets, and then calculate the total cost of this part of their trip, taking various concessions into account. In doing so, they will need to select the correct information from a range of sources.

Questions to consider
- *What is the Edinburgh Military Tattoo?*
- *How would you book tickets to a concert?*
- *What is a concession?*

Answers
1 22nd August
2 a) Sunday or Monday
  b) £28 × 0.9 = £25.20
3 (£25 + £3) × 2 = £56
4 £56 + £25.20 + £28 + (£35 × 2) = £179.20

Ⓑ Getting there

The emphasis in this section is on extracting information from tables and maps to solve the problems involved in planning a complex journey. The starting place and destination require a journey across London in a limited amount of time, and students have to decide which of two options is better. This will require some understanding of the probability of transport running smoothly in a large city. It may be helpful to discuss what happens to traffic during the morning rush hour.

Answers
1 Journey times are: 6h 21 mins, 6h 13 mins, 6h 20 mins and 6h 50 mins.
  So they should catch the 8:41 train.
2 Time from 9:44 to 10:30 = 46 minutes.
3 Using measurement from the map and scale, allow between 4.2 km and 4.4 km.
4 Min: 4.2 ÷ 8 × 60 = 31.5 mins
  Max: 4.4 ÷ 8 × 60 = 33 mins. Allow answers within this range.
  Yes, if the taxi travels at the average speed.
5 Shortest time 31.5 mins ≈ 32 mins
  Time after which highest rate is needed
  = (8.60 − 1.40) ÷ 20 = 36 mins
  £1.40 + 32 × £0.20 = £7.80. Allow answers in the range £7.70 – £8.00 if given with the correct working out.
6 a) (21 × 3 + 20 + 35) ÷ 5 = 23.6 mins ≈ 24 mins
  b) Most realistic choice is the underground as it is quicker. Taxi unlikely to take minimum time as it may not always be moving, so could be more expensive.

C Where to stay?

Here students need to decide which of the four hotels is cheapest by comparing the cost of the hotel with other costs for transport and food. It is a much less structured task than the previous sections, with all the information given at the start. The questions help to structure a route to the answer and model one method of breaking down a task into manageable pieces. There is less structure as the questions progress but the problems are similar so students can use a similar method.

Answers

1 It is fully booked for all but one of the dates they want to stay for.
2 a) $1.5 \times 8 \div 5 = 2.4$ km $= 2400$ m
   b) 2400 m $- 450$ m $= 1950$ m < 2000 m, so using middle rate $1950 \div 200 \approx 10$ (rounded up).
       £1.60 + 10 × £0.25 = £4.10 per trip; 10 trips = £41
   c) £160 × 4 + £41 + £25 × 8 = £881
3 a) £10 more; £5.10 per trip so a total of £51
   b) 4 nights plus 2 breakfasts and 2 dinners each night plus taxis:
       (£100 + 2 × £10 + 2 × £25) × 4 + £51 = £731
4 Alba House is cheapest; Parliament House Hotel costs 200 × 4 = £800 (includes dinner, breakfast and no taxis needed), Alba House costs £731, Victoria Park House Hotel costs £881.

D Vicki's new kilt

This section is made up of a single question with all required information in a variety of forms. The question requires students to plan their method in order to find the solution. It may be helpful to make it clear to students that the number of pleats mentioned in the second bullet means the length of the pleat section.

Answer

1 Converting Vicki's measurements to inches –
   Hip measurement 105 cm ÷ 2.5 = 42 inches.
   So pleat section is 21 inches and each apron is 21 inches.
   Amount of material: length of each pleat, L = 2 × 4 + 1 = 9 inches.
   So for 21 inches of pleats, that uses 9 × 21 = 189 inches.
   For the aprons = 2 × 21 inches = 42 inches of material.
   So total length needed = 189 + 42 = 231 inches.
   Converting to metric units gives 231 × 2.5 = 577.5 cm = 5.775 m
   Plus 10% = 5.775 × 1.1 = 6.3525 ≈ 7 m (rounding up to the nearest metre)
   Total cost: (7 × £39 + 2 × £5 + £100) × 1.15 + £36.99 + £25 = £502.44

Assessment – Successful completion of this unit should provide evidence for assessment in these areas.		
	NC Level 5	**NC Level 6**
Using and applying mathematics	Identify and obtain necessary information to carry through a task and solve mathematical problems	Solve problems and carry through substantial tasks by breaking them into smaller, more manageable tasks, using a range of efficient techniques, methods and resources, including ICT; give solutions to an appropriate degree of accuracy
Number	Understand simple ratios	Use the equivalence of fractions, decimals and percentages to compare proportions
Calculating	Use a calculator where appropriate to calculate fractions/percentages of quantities/measurements Solve simple problems involving ratio and direct proportion	Calculate percentages and find the outcome of a given percentage increase or decrease Divide a quantity into two or more parts in a given ratio and solve problems involving ratio and direct proportion
Shape, space and measure	Solve problems involving the conversion of units and make sensible estimates of a range of measures in relation to everyday situations	
Algebra	Construct, express in symbolic form, and use simple formulae involving one or two operations	
Handling data	In probability, select methods based on equally likely outcomes and experimental evidence, as appropriate	Communicate interpretations and results of a statistical survey using selected tables, graphs and diagrams in support

Unit 2 – Managing the Supermarket

Overview

This unit considers different aspects of managing a supermarket and focuses specifically on the bakery. It requires students to put themselves in the position of the manager and decide how much stock they should provide. Students look at the cost of producing items made in-store, and consider how stock should be organised. Finally, they suggest the profit made on a particular day by making informed predictions based on previous data.

Key vocabulary

trend, line of best fit, maximum, minimum, average, sample, scale, profit

Objectives

Students should focus on developing different aspects of their Using and Applying mathematics skills throughout the unit.

A – L6: Interpret, discuss and synthesise information presented in a variety of mathematical forms

B – L5: Check results, considering whether these are reasonable

C – L5: Draw simple conclusions of their own and give an explanation of their reasoning

D – L6: Present a concise, reasoned argument, using symbols, diagrams, graphs and related explanatory texts

A Number of sales

This section uses data to speculate on the amount spent and number of items purchased by each customer. This information is used to predict how much stock should be produced by the in-store bakery.

Questions to consider
- *What do supermarkets sell?*
- *Who decides what the supermarket will sell?*
- *What does a store manager have responsibility for?*

Answers
1 Approximately £102 using line of best fit (allow between 80 and 120 for variance between maximum and minimum lines).

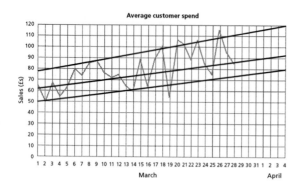

2 Using mean 36.3 ≈ 36, using median 36.5 ≈ 37
3 Accept answers between £26.40 and £39.60; answer to Qu 1 × 0.33.
4 Three items; using the average number of items from Qu 2: 36 × 0.07 = 2.52, or 37 × 0.07 = 2.59.

B The bakery

This section focuses on the quantity of bakery products that should be produced and consequently the quantity of ingredients needed. Students also consider any time management issues in producing this stock. Both the quantity needed and the time management issues have an impact on the cost of producing an item and the reasoning behind this may be worth discussing with the class during the activity.

Answers
1 3500 ÷ 7 × 3 = 1500
2 rolls = 29%
   1500 × 0.29 = 435 rolls
3 wholemeal = 22%
   435 × 0.22 = 95.7 ≈ 96 rolls
4 a) 500 g × (96 ÷ 12) = 4 kg
   b) The baker mixes and kneads each batch one after the other. This takes 40 mins. After 70 mins the first four batches go in the oven for 20 mins. When they have finished, the next four batches are ready to cook and take another 20 mins. Overall, the time it takes to cook the eight batches will be 70 + 20 + 20 = 110 mins = 1 hour and 50 mins.
   Encourage use of a timeline to make sense of the overlapping times.

5

Item	Kg needed	Pack weight (kg)	Pack cost	Cost
Wholemeal flour	4	16	£9.99	£2.50
Butter	0.08	0.25	£0.99	£0.32
Salt	0.08	3	£1.70	£0.05
Yeast	0.16	1	£9.00	£1.44
			Total cost	£4.31

C Displaying the bakery products

In this section, students calculate how much of the display area is required for different bakery products. The questions provide a route to the final answer. It may be helpful to draw students' attention to the range of information given at the beginning, including the dimensions of the products and shelving. It would also be useful to discuss the different shapes of each product and relate them to solids. This will allow revision of methods for finding volumes.

Answers

1. a) roll: $\pi \times 4^2 \times 4 = 201.06 \, \text{cm}^3$
      bagel: $\pi \times 4.5^2 \times 3 = 190.85 \, \text{cm}^3$
   b) bread bin volume = $40 \times 60 \times 30$
      = $72,000 \, \text{cm}^3$
      $72,000 \div 201.06 = 358.09 \approx 358$ rolls
   c) $358 > 320$ and bagels are smaller than rolls so all of one type of roll/bagel will fit into one bread bin. So answer is yes.
2. $2.4 \times 4 + 6 = 15.6 \, \text{m}$, as there are 4 shelves on either side of the bread bins plus one full length shelf above them.
3. a) 120 boxes; 1 m by 0.5 m of shelf will fit 4×10 boxes in each layer.
      $4 \times 10 \times 3 = 120$ boxes
   b) 0.5 m
4. Cakes: $0.3 \, \text{m} \times 20 = 6 \, \text{m}$, doughnuts: 0.5 m total 6.5 m used so 9.1 m left for loaves of bread.
5. Assuming that loaves are placed with the longest edge parallel to the edge of the shelf. Each shelf can fit $50 \div 6.5 \approx 7$ loaves deep. The 9.1 m of shelves can have 36 loaves on them. So total loaves = $7 \times 36 = 252$ loaves
   Ratio of production for
   white : wholemeal : other is 760 : 240 : 75.
   392 into this ratio gives the following number of loaves:
   white: 178 wholemeal: 56 other: 18

D Expected profit

The last section of the unit focuses on predicting how much profit will be made by the in-store bakery. Using the approximate costs of production, quantity produced and data about customers, students calculate expected revenue and compare this to the costs involved. It would be helpful to discuss the differences between expected and actual values involved, so that students appreciate that all costs must be covered, regardless of how many items one expects to sell. This task also raises the importance of appropriate rounding, as the number of some products is too low to register for an individual customer but will have value when the sales are all taken as a whole. The problem is unstructured and will require careful planning and the identification of a successful process.

Answer

1. Using a line of best fit, the graph suggests there will be approximately 480 customers on 10th May.
   Each customer will probably buy 2 items = $2 \times 480 = 960$ items.

Product	Proportion of each product sold	Potential sales	Stock	Number sold	Revenue	Cost	Profit
Bread – Loaf	72%	691	600	600	£684.00	£395.00	£289.00
Bread – Roll	7%	67	250	67	£40.20	£13.19	£27.01
Bagel	4%	38	50	38	£28.50	£0.80	£27.70
Doughnuts	5%	48 approx. 10 packs	20 packs	10	£10.00	£4.00	£6.00
Cake	12%	115	12	12	£47.88	£12.60	£35.28
						Total profit	£384.99

Assessment – Successful completion of this unit should provide evidence for assessment in these areas.

	NC Level 5	NC Level 6
Using and applying mathematics	Draw simple conclusions of their own and give an explanation of their reasoning	Present a concise, reasoned argument, using symbols, diagrams, graphs and related explanatory texts
Number	Use equivalence between fractions and order fractions and decimals	Use the equivalence of fractions, decimals and percentages to compare proportions
Calculating	Use a calculator where appropriate to calculate fractions/percentages of quantities/measurements	Add and subtract fractions by writing them with a common denominator, calculate fractions of quantities (fraction answers), multiply and divide an integer by a fraction
Calculate percentages and find the outcome of a given percentage increase or decrease
Shape, space and measure	Solve problems involving the conversion of units and make sensible estimates of a range of measures in relation to everyday situations	Deduce and use formulae for the area of a triangle and parallelogram, and the volume of a cuboid; calculate volumes and surface areas of cuboids
Visualise and use 2-D representations of 3-D objects
Handling data	Ask questions, plan how to answer them and collect the data required	Communicate interpretations and results of a statistical survey using selected tables, graphs and diagrams in support

Unit 3 – Festival

Overview

This unit focuses on issues surrounding the planning of a local music festival and uses familiar and unfamiliar settings to develop students' ability to apply their methods in different situations. The unit starts by considering how the cost and weather affects a family attending the festival, and then goes on to look at the practical aspects of setting up and managing a festival, including stage design and event facilities.

Key vocabulary

probability, maximum, minimum, trend, expected value, average, area, projection

Objectives

Students should focus on developing different aspects of their Using and Applying mathematics skills throughout the unit.

A – L5: Identify and obtain necessary information to carry through a task and solve mathematical problems

B – L5: Check results, considering whether these are reasonable

C – L5: Show understanding of situations by describing them mathematically using symbols, words and diagrams

D – L6: Solve problems and carry through substantial tasks by breaking them into smaller, more manageable tasks, using a range of efficient techniques, methods and resources, including ICT

A Rainy day?

This section starts by looking at the cost for a family to visit a festival and considers the preparations that the family would make prior to attending, taking the probable weather into account.

Questions to consider

- *Is this an expensive weekend for the family?*
- *Why does the family care about the weather?*
- *How might different types of weather affect the family's plans?*

Answers

1 Family pass = £30 × 3 = £90
  Campsite – need to pay for 5 people –
  5 × 2 × £14 = £140
  £90 + £140 = £210
2 5 out of 10 days rain above normal so 50%, $\frac{1}{2}$ or 0.5
3 Using maximum and minimum values from graph: min ≈ 4°C, max ≈ 18°C
4 On all of the data recorded, the min values are below 9°C so probability = 1
5 (answer to min from Qu 3) – 8 ≈ – 4°C

B The stage

This section asks students to put themselves into the position of a stage designer to determine if the proposed stage is adequate to accommodate all bands at the festival. As an unfamiliar situation, this extends the complexity of the problem, although the drawings are designed to look similar to those seen previously. The problem is broken down into steps to model the process techniques required.

Questions to consider

- *What process did the questions lead you through?*
- *Is there a more efficient way that you could have done this task?*

Answers

1 12 × 4 + (12 + 8) × (6 – 4) ÷ 2 = 68 m²
2 6 × 2 = 12 m²
3 3 × π × 1.5² ≈ 21.2 m²
4 Keyboard players: 2 × (1.5 × 3 + 1.5 × 0.5)
  = 10.5 m²
  Drummers: 2 × $\frac{1}{2}$ × π × 2² ≈ 12.6 m²
  Backing singers: 4 × π × 1² ≈ 12.6 m²
  Total area = 10.5 + 2 × 12.6 + 21.2 + 12 ≈ 68.9 m² rounding up
5 a) 68.9 × 1.125 = 77.5 m²
  b) No; they need 77.5 m² but only have 68 m².

C Lighting the stage

This section takes an unusual look at a spatial problem, which combines finding the cheapest solution using the rental prices given whilst balancing the spatial understanding of where the lights can be positioned against their coverage.

Questions to consider

- *How else could you have answered Qu 3?*

Answers

1 80 m²
2 a) 2($\frac{1}{4}$ × π × 2²) + 3 × 2 ≈ 12.3 m²
  b) 2; these will only cover the back and front areas of the stage (they are expensive).
  c) 80 – 2 × 12.3 ≈ 55.4 m²

d) Area of spotlight = π × 3² ≈ 28.3 m²,
so two might cover the area left but
this doesn't allow for the stage shape.
Considering the positions of the power
points gives a minimum of two strip
lights and four spotlights.

3

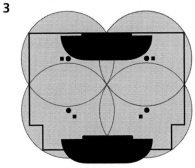

4 [(200 × 2 + 4 × 10) × 2] × 1.15 = £1012

Festival sales

This final section focuses on further facilities
at the festival but remains in an unfamiliar
context. Whilst students will be aware of
purchasing, they need to look at the problem
from an organiser's perspective. The question is
unstructured and will require careful planning
and the identification of a successful process.

Answer

1 15,000 attendance last year, reduced by
15% to give 12,750 attendees.
Half bought clothes = 6375 sales
45% brought food = 5737.5 ≈ 5737 sales
3.6 drinks per person = 45,900 sales
Assume hot food sales do not include
ice-cream.

Bite to Eat		
Item	**Sales**	**Revenue**
Jacket potatoes	1,434	£5,004.66
Pizza	1,075	£5,364.25
Burgers	3,227	£9,648.73
Ice-cream	1,275	£2,550.00
Tea	15,300	£19,125.00
Coffee	22,950	£28,687.50
Chocolate	7,650	£11,475.00
Total revenue		£81,855.14

Wrap and Roll Clothing		
Item	**Sales**	**Revenue**
Kagool	4271	£106,732.29
Jumpers/Sweatshirts	2103	£84,098.97
Wellies	4590	£45,900.00
Sun hats	200	£1,200.00
Total revenue		£237,931.26

Rental on current system – £2000 plus 3% of
revenue

Wrap and Roll rental	£9,137.94
Bite to Eat rental	£4,455.65
Total rental	£13,593.59

Rental on proposed system – 4% of revenue

Total revenue	£319, 786.40
Rental at 4%	£12,791.46

The rental on the current system is more so
they should leave it as it is.

Assessment – Successful completion of this unit should provide evidence for assessment in these areas.		
	NC Level 5	**NC Level 6**
Using and applying mathematics	Identify and obtain necessary information to carry through a task and solve mathematical problems	Solve problems and carry through substantial tasks by breaking them into smaller, more manageable tasks, using a range of efficient techniques, methods and resources, including ICT
Number	Use equivalence between fractions and order fractions and decimals	Use the equivalence of fractions, decimals and percentages to compare proportions
Calculating	Add and subtract fractions by writing them with a common denominator, calculate fractions of quantities, multiply and divide an integer by a fraction Solve simple problems involving ordering, adding, subtracting negative numbers in context	Calculate percentages and find the outcome of a given percentage increase or decrease
Algebra	Construct, express in symbolic form, and use simple formulae involving one or two operations	
Shape, space and measure	Understand and use the formula for the area of a rectangle and distinguish area from perimeter Use a wider range of properties of 2-D and 3-D shapes and identify all the symmetries of 2-D shapes	Deduce and use formulae for the area of a triangle and parallelogram, and the volume of a cuboid; calculate volumes and surface areas of cuboids. Visualise and use 2-D representations of 3-D objects
Handling data	In probability, select methods based on equally likely outcomes and experimental evidence, as appropriate	

Unit 4 – Finance for living

Overview

This unit follows Rakesh through some major financial phases of his life, including funding his education choices and later deciding whether to buy or rent when moving away from home. This topic has direct links with the PSHE unit covering budgeting and money management. Rakesh's financial responsibilities and rights are outlined using realistic and accurate in methods and figures.

Key vocabulary

percentage, fraction, interest rate, net, gross, deduction, APR, expenses, loan, grant

Objectives

Students should focus on developing different aspects of their Using and Applying mathematics skills throughout the unit.

A – L5: Identify and obtain necessary information to carry through a task and solve mathematical problems

B – L6: Interpret, discuss and synthesise information presented in a variety of mathematical forms

C – L5: Check results, considering whether these are reasonable

D – L6: Present a concise, reasoned argument, using symbols, diagrams, graphs and related explanatory texts

A Leaving school

This section follows the choices Rakesh makes as he prepares for Sixth Form College. The inclusion of information on EMAs highlights the existence of financial support as young people move towards financial independence.

Questions to consider
- *What choices do you have at 16?*
- *What expenses might you have that you didn't have before?*
- *How old do you need to be to get a job?*
- *Why do we have to pay taxes?*

Answers
1 Yes; he will be on a full-time course.
2 He is eligible for £20 a week; household income = £24,500.
3 2 + 3.5 + 2 + 5.5 = 13 hours
4 £4.45 × 13 + £13.20 = £71.05
5 Weekly tax allowance = 6475 ÷ 52 ≈ £124.52, weekly National Insurance allowance = £95. Rakesh earns below both limits so doesn't need to pay Income Tax or National Insurance.

B Gap year

It is quite normal for young people to take a break in their studies, to work or travel. In this section, Rakesh has a working gap year which allows him to discover his responsibilities as a citizen through paying Income Tax and National Insurance, as well as contributing to the household.

During this activity, it is likely that students will need to discuss the details of Income Tax and National Insurance. This section only considers one level of taxation, but students may be interested in what happens if you earn a larger income.

Answers
1 a) 35 hours
  b) 35 × £5.95 = £208.25
2 (£208.25 – £95) × 0.11 = £12.46
3 a) £208.25 – (£6745 ÷ 52) = £78.54
  b) £78.54 × 0.2 = £15.71
4 £208.25 – (£12.46 + £15.71) = £180.08
5 Expenses = £670, divided between 5 people and 4 weeks:
  £670 ÷ 5 ÷ 4 = £33.50
  £180.08 – £33.50 = £146.58

C University

The section looks at university education and the questions focus on the financial situation of students at university and college. Although the topic is unfamiliar at this stage, many students may have knowledge of this area through discussions with family or friends. The information is detailed and realistic in terms of the amount of loan or grant provided to support students, as well as the reality of means-testing students, and family support. Whilst it would be unwise to focus on the differences between family support, it is a reality that students will need to consider when making choices about further education.

Answers

1. a) £3225 + £3800 = £7025
   b) £4950 – 0.5 × £2906 = £3497
   c) £2906 + £3497 = £6403
   d) £6403 – £3225 = £3178 (not enough left to cover rent, £622 short)
2. 15 × £5.35 = £80.25
3. a) £80.25 × 30 + (–£622) = £1785.50
   b) £1785.50 ÷ 30 ≈ £59.52

D Where to live?

This last section focuses on making decisions about whether to rent or buy property. Students will calculate the costs per person of a group of friends sharing, using information that is provided in a variety of forms. This section allows the application of known methods in an unfamiliar situation. The task is unstructured and so students need to plan their method. Whilst they should consider the task from a purely mathematical point of view, discussions about the pros and cons of buying and renting would make an interesting plenary.

Answer

1. Renting: £645 ÷ 3 = £215 each.
   Buying: share per person £165,000 ÷ 3
   = £55,000
   Deposit per person: £55,000 × 0.15 = £8250
   Mortgage amount per person:
   £55,000 – £8250 = £46,750
   Monthly payment: £46,750 × 3.6 ÷ 100 × $\frac{1}{7}$
   ≈ £240.43
   So it is cheaper to rent than buy.

Assessment – Successful completion of this unit should provide evidence for assessment in these areas.

	NC Level 5	NC Level 6
Using and applying mathematics	Check results, considering whether these are reasonable	Present a concise, reasoned argument, using symbols, diagrams, graphs and related explanatory texts
Number	Use equivalence between fractions and order fractions and decimals	
Calculating		Add and subtract fractions by writing them with a common denominator, calculate fractions of quantities (fraction answers), multiply and divide an integer by a fraction Calculate percentages and find the outcome of a given percentage increase or decrease
Handling data	Interpret graphs and diagrams, including pie charts, and draw conclusions	Communicate interpretations and results of a statistical survey using selected tables, graphs and diagrams in support

Unit 5 – Building a conservatory

Overview

This unit covers progressive aspects of building a conservatory, from the initial design process through to calculating the materials needed, finding the cost of materials and finally comparing two different flooring options.

The final task provides an opportunity to use ICT to model the costing of a project using a spreadsheet.

Key vocabulary

symmetrical, views, isometric, conversion, area, volume, VAT

Objectives

Students should focus on developing different aspects of their Using and Applying mathematics skills throughout the unit.

A – L5: Show understanding of situations by describing them mathematically using symbols, words and diagrams

B – L5: Solve word problems and investigations from a range of contexts

C – L6: Give solutions to an appropriate degree of accuracy

D – L6: Solve problems and carry through substantial tasks by breaking them into smaller, more manageable tasks, using a range of efficient techniques, methods and resources, including ICT

A Design

This section focuses on the design of a conservatory. This allows students time to develop confidence in the theme whilst setting an appropriate challenge for level 2. Thus the design isn't straightforward but requires some thought to complete the drawings.

Questions to consider

- *What does a conservatory look like?*
- *What different styles of conservatory have you seen?*
- *What materials are used in constructing a conservatory?*
- *Can anyone add a conservatory to their house?*
- *Why are some buildings symmetrical?*

Having a range of images to discuss on an interactive whiteboard or projector would support this discussion.

Answers

The drawings for Qu 1 should approximate to those shown below, allowing for different heights on the front and side views. Drawings are acceptable with or without lines for the windows shown.

1

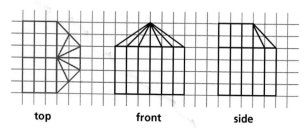

top   front   side

2   **3**   **4**

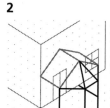 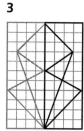 

The design wi**l** need at least 3 colours.

B What materials will be needed?

This section focuses on calculating the materials needed to construct the foundation base and walls for a brick-based design. Students need to calculate area and volume based on the drawing from Qu 1 and then use the additional information to work out the amount of each material needed. It would be helpful to highlight that relevant information can be found both prior to and within the questions themselves, before students attempt the activity.

It may be worth discussing how big each square is in centimetres and working out the other lengths before students start answering the questions.

Answers

1 a) 9.36 m²
   b) $V = 9.36 \times 0.5 = 4.68$ m³
   c) $4.68 \times 2500 = 11{,}700$ kg
2 a) $W = 55 \times 11{,}700 \div 900 = 715$ litres
   b) $715 \div 4.5 = 158.8 \approx 159$ gallons
3 a) $1.8 \times 2 + 1.7 \times 2 + 1.2 = 8.2$ m
   b) 8200 mm
   c) $8200 \div 220 = 37.27 \approx 38$ (allow 37.5)
4 $38 \times 6 = 228$ (225)
5 456 bricks (450)

C Cost of materials

This section looks at the costs of materials for building a conservatory. All information is provided at the start of the section so students need to identify what is relevant to complete the task. The route to the answer is structured through the questions and models one method for breaking down a task into manageable pieces. Students should find this useful in the final section of this unit. Encourage students to use information from the previous section when selecting the correct size of French doors.

Answers

Note: Students may have their own solution method that differs from that given here. Their methods may also be correct but the following presents the most efficient solution.

1 a) 3 for 2 deal – pay for four 600 mm (@£180 each) and three 850 mm (@£360) 4 × 180 + 3 × 360 = £1800
   b) 500 × £0.35 × 1.15 = £201.25
   550 × £0.35 = £192.50
   £8.75 saving

2

Materials	Quantity	Cheapest cost inc. VAT
Ready-to-mix concrete	5 m³	£2242.50
Bricks	1 pallet	£192.50
Mortar	18 bags	£72.45
Windows 60 cm wide	6	£720
Windows 85 cm wide	4	£1080
French doors 1200 mm	1 pair	£400
Guttering	10 m	£100

3 £4807.45

D Floor design

The final section of the unit is the least structured and looks at choosing the cheapest floor solution from two offered. There is a wealth of information followed by a single question. Students need to plan a strategy to answer the question. They will need to justify their answer using their calculations.

Answer

1 Floor area + 10% = 10.3 m²
   Floor edging + 10% = 12,980 mm

Tiled Floor
Tiles: 10.3 ÷ 0.9 = 11.4 ≈ 12 boxes
12 × £20 = £240
Grout: 2 × £11.98 = £23.96
Adhesive: 10.3 ÷ 1.8 = 5.72 ≈ 6 tubs
6 × £19.50 × 0.75 = £87.75
Total cost = £351.71

Laminate Floor
Laminate: 10.3 ÷ 2.7 = 3.8 ≈ 4 boxes
4 × £16 = £84
Kit: £18.99
Adhesive: £3.55 × 2 × 1.15 = 8.165 ≈ £8.17
Edging: 12,980 ÷ 900 = 14.4 ≈ 15
15 × £0.50 × 1.15 ≈ £8.63
Underlay: £9.76 × 2 × 1.15 = £22.45
Total cost = £142.24

Total cost tiles = £351.71
Total cost laminate = £142.24
Ivan should use laminate flooring.

Assessment – Successful completion of this unit should provide evidence for assessment in these areas.

	NC Level 5	NC Level 6
Using and applying mathematics	Solve word problems and investigations from a range of contexts	Solve problems and carry through substantial tasks by breaking them into smaller, more manageable tasks, using a range of efficient techniques, methods and resources, including ICT; give solutions to an appropriate degree of accuracy
Number	Use equivalence between fractions and order fractions and decimals	Use the equivalence of fractions, decimals and percentages to compare proportions
Calculating	Solve simple problems involving ratio and direct proportion	Add and subtract fractions by writing them with a common denominator, calculate fractions of quantities (fraction answers), multiply and divide an integer by a fraction
Divide a quantity into two or more parts in a given ratio and solve problems involving ratio and direct proportion
Algebra	Construct, express in symbolic form, and use simple formulae involving one or two operations	
Shape, space and measure	Understand and use the formula for the area of a rectangle and distinguish area from perimeter
Solve problems involving the conversion of units and make sensible estimates of a range of measures in relation to everyday situations	Visualise and use 2-D representations of 3-D objects

Answers to review exercises

Entry 3 – Level 1
Number and algebra

NA1
1 a) Four hundred and fifty six
  b) Seven hundred and sixty five
  c) Eight hundred and ninety nine
  d) Three hundred and twenty one
  e) Nine hundred and eighty one
  f) Eight hundred and seventy one
  g) Two hundred and ninety one
  h) Nine hundred and eighty eight
  i) Eight hundred and thirty four

2 a) 334   b) 686   c) 520   d) 809

NA2
1 a) 75   b) 104   c) 44   d) 8
  e) 540   f) 384   g) 3   h) 4

NA3
1 a) 558   b) 459   c) 1023
2 a) 135   b) 431   c) 115

NA4
1 £70   2 10   3 30   4 10

NA5
1 a) 24   b) 16   c) 10   d) 12
  e) 36   f) 40   g) 45   h) 20
  i) 50

NA6
1 a) 80   b) 70   c) 50   d) 90
  e) 100   f) 430   g) 880   h) 780
  i) 980

2 a) 200   b) 200   c) 300   d) 400
  e) 900   f) 3600   g) 6600   h) 7600
  i) 8700

NA7
1 a) £15   b) 25 lb   c) 60 kg   d) $11
  e) £25   f) £12

NA8
1 a) £1.50   b) £2.75   c) £12.90   d) £345.20

NA9
1 a) adding 2, even numbers/multiples of 2
  b) adding 5, multiples of 5
  c) adding 2, odd numbers
  d) adding previous difference +1 each time,
     triangular numbers
  e) adding 4, multiples of 4
  f) adding 10, multiples of 10

Shape, space and measures
SSM1

Item	Estimate
Width of your bedroom	2–5 m
Time to walk a mile	15–25 minutes
Weight of average adult	30–80 kg
Height of your house	4–10 m
Capacity of a tea cup	100–200 ml

SSM2
1 a) £12.50   b) £3.50   c) £15   d) £155
2 a) 1300 ml   b) 3 m   c) 44 km   d) 25 kg

SSM3
1 a) circle   b) rectangle
  c) isosceles triangle   d) square
  e) hexagon   f) pentagon
  g) scalene triangle
2 a) cylinder   b) cube
  c) cone   d) cuboid

SSM4
1 a) cm   b) g
  c) miles/km   d) kg
  e) m   f) inches
  g) mm

Handling data

1 a) 12   b) 10   c) 24 − 8 = 16
2 a) swimming   b) 7   c) 30
3 a) January   b) May

Level 1
Number and algebra

A1

Moscow

Melbourne

Moscow, Paris, New York, Berlin, London,
Hong Kong, Melbourne

a) 5°C   b) 7°C   c) 1°C   d) 6°C

A2

a) 17   b) 49

a) 9   b) 22

a) 28   b) 204

a) 9   b) 22

a) 567   b) 305

a) 432   b) 408

A3

a) 80   b) 170

a) 3   b) 12

a) 3.5   b) 12.4

a) 12,400   b) 24,500

a) 12   b) 24

a) 20   b) 5000

A4

Fraction	Decimal	Percentage
$\frac{1}{2}$	0.5	50%
$\frac{1}{4}$	0.25	25%
$\frac{1}{10}$	0.1	10%
$\frac{3}{10}$	0.3	30%
$\frac{3}{4}$	0.75	75%
$\frac{4}{10}$ or $\frac{2}{5}$	0.4	40%

A5

1 1.77   **2** 0.31   **3** 1.67   **4** 0.07

A6

£21, £35

£28, £35

£30, £42

A7

a) T = 30   b) T = 48   c) T = 72

a) T = 30   b) T = 45   c) T = 60

Shape, space and measures

SSM1

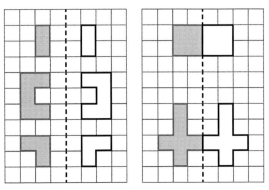

SSM2

1 a) area = 9 cm², perimeter = 12 cm

    b) area = 14 cm², perimeter = 18 cm

    c) area = 12 cm², perimeter = 24 cm

SSM3

1 A = 35   B = 38   C = 48

2 A = 300   B = 380   C = 480

Handling data

HD1

1 a) mean = 7

    b) mean = 31

2 mean = 140 cm

3 mean = £200

4 a) range = 17

    b) range = 16

    c) range = 40

HD2

1 a) 25

    b) cheese and onion

    c) 5

HD3

1

Temperature °C	Tally	Frequency
8	I	1
9	I	1
10	II	2
11	III	3
12	IIII	4
13	III	3

HD4

1 green

2 yellow

Level 1 – Level 2
Number and algebra

NA1
1 a) $13 \times 10 = 130$
c) $43.567 \times 100 = 4356.7$
b) $13.4 \times 100 = 1340$
d) $6.6597 \times 1000 = 6659.7$
2 a) $256 \div 10 = 25.6$
c) $95{,}800 \div 100 = 958$
b) $25.6 \div 10 = 2.56$
d) $95{,}800 \div 1000 = 95.8$

NA2
1 a) $25.68 \approx 25.7$
b) $468.059 \approx 468.1$
c) $12.0035 \approx 12.0$
2 $-11°C, -8°C, -3°C, -2°C, 0°C, 6°C, 9°C, 11°C, 12°C$

NA3
1 $\frac{5}{20}, \frac{6}{20}, \frac{7}{20}, \frac{8}{20}, \frac{10}{20}, \frac{12}{20}, \frac{15}{20}$
2 $\frac{9}{10}, 0.68, 0.52, 0.486, \frac{7}{15}, \frac{3}{8}, 0.2, 0.127$

NA4
1 a) $\frac{3}{5}$ b) $\frac{3}{5}$ c) $\frac{3}{4}$ d) $\frac{8}{11}$

NA5
1 $120 : 180$ **2** $3 : 4$

NA6
1 $5(12.6 - 3 \times 1.45) + 15 \div 5 = 44.25$
2 $5 + 7 \times 1.25 - 18 \div 0.5 = -22.25$

NA7
1 65.83 **2** 290.36
3 2.92 m **4** 351 kg

NA8
1 8544 **2** 73,154
3 9 **4** 72

NA9
1 $23 - (-14) = 37°C$
2 $(-7) + 12 = 5°C$
3 $£23 - £39.99 = -£16.99$, so it is overdrawn.

NA10
1 $8000 \text{ cm} = 80 \text{ m}$ **2** $1000 \text{ g} = 1 \text{ kg}$

NA11
1 $9 \times 4 - 12 = 24$ **2** $(185 - 50) \div 15 = 9$

NA12
1 $2a - b = 180$
2 Any values from this table.

a	b	a	b	a	b	a	b	a	b	a	b
91	2	96	12	101	22	106	32	111	42	116	52
92	4	97	14	102	24	107	34	112	44	117	54
93	6	98	16	103	26	108	36	113	46	118	56
94	8	99	18	104	28	109	38	114	48	119	58
95	10	100	20	105	30	110	40	115	50		

Shape, space and measures
SSM1

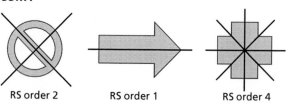

RS order 2 RS order 1 RS order 4

RS order 8 RS order 5

SSM2
1 An equilateral triangle drawn with 60° corners and any length of side.
2 Triangle as shown here:

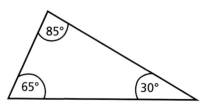

SSM3
1 47 kg and 140 g respectively

SSM4
1 1700 m
2 $3600 \text{ g} = 3.6 \text{ kg}$
3 2 m

SSM5
1 $A = 4.5 \times 0.8 = 3.6 \text{ m}^2$, $P = (4.5 + 0.8) \times 2 = 10.6 \text{ m}$
2 Any values from this table.

l	w	area	l	w	area
1	19	19	6	14	84
2	18	36	7	13	91
3	17	51	8	12	96
4	16	64	9	11	99
5	15	75	10	10	100

Handling data
HD1
1 Count the number of chairs in each room (sample of rooms). Tally the totals and compare.
2 Students to undergo a survey on the number of chairs in each room.

HD2

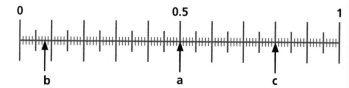

)3

13.22

Accept either with appropriate reason.

)4

Road A has lots of pedestrians and bicycles, so is probably in a town centre. The lack of lorries suggest it has controlled traffic. Road B is more likely to be a main road into a town centre or a busy village, as it has more lorries and buses and less bicycles and pedestrians.

Accept any similar answers as long as the reasoning is sound.

)5

The graph shows that 85 Krona is approximately £7.10.

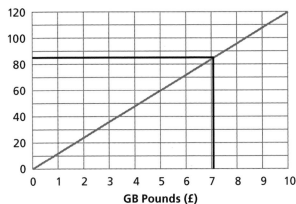

Conversion rates for Swedish Krona and GB Pounds

D6

234 miles

Aberdeen = 494 miles, Norwich = 245 miles

494 − 245 = 249 miles

evel 2

umber and algebra

A1

$\frac{17}{20}$ **2** $\frac{11}{60}$

A2

60   **2** 63   **3** 294

A3

9   **2** 45   **3** £19.12

A4

150   **2** 110.7   **3** 349.2

A5

250 × 1.2 = 300

145 × 0.95 = 137.75

A6

75 ÷ 5 = 15   30 : 45

240 ÷ 8 = 30   30 : 90 : 120

£540 ÷ 8 = £67.50   £337.50 : £202.50

4 × 600 = 2400 mm = 2.4 m

NA7

1 One third of 40 = 13.33

40% of 35 = 14

0.9 × 15 = 13.5

So 40% of 15 is bigger.

NA8

1 −5 + 7 = 2°C

2 £29.45 − £35 = −£5.55 (a loss)

NA9

1 a) 4 × −5 = −20

b) 3 + 5 × 21 = 3 + 105 = 108

2 a) P = 2(11 + 5) = 2 × 16 = 32

b) P = 2(2 + 0.25) = 2 × 2.25 = 4.5

c) P = 2(87 + 250) = 2 × 337 = 674 cm = 6.74 m

Shape, space and measures

SSM1

1 a) area = 40 m²   perimeter = 26 m

b) area = 12 × 4.6 + 9.5 × 5.4 = 106.5 m²

perimeter = 44 m

c) area = 120 × 80 × $\frac{1}{2}$ = 4800 cm² = 480 m²

perimeter = 3.2 m

2 C = 12 × π ≈ 37.7 mm

3 A = π × 6² ≈ 113.1 mm²

SSM2, SSM3

1 a) 5 × 4 × 3 = 60 cm³

b) ($\frac{1}{2}$ × 6 × 8) × 12 = 288 mm³

c) (π × 4²) × 9 ≈ 452 m²

SSM4

1 45 ÷ 1.8 = £25

2 15 ÷ 0.3 = 50 feet

3 98 × 4.5 = 441p = £4.41

4 Cyclist travels 16 mph.

Sprinter travels 600 metres per minute = 36 km/h

36 × 5 ÷ 8 = 22.5 mph, so the sprinter is fastest.

Handling data

HD1

1 a) Negative correlation. Accept a statement that the more rainfall there is the fewer hours of sunshine per day there are.

b) 4 – 6 mm depending on line of best fit.

2 a) 480 − 230 = 250 (allow 240 – 270)

b) Total for year, stall ≈ 800

Total for year, shop ≈ 1400

The shop makes more.

c) Freak cold spell, bad weather so shop and stall may have had to close for some reason.

HD2

1 a) 30 ≤ t < 40

b) 50 ≤ t < 60

c) Any reasonable answer is acceptable.

HD3

1 $\frac{6}{10}$ or 60% or equivalent

Functional skills self assessment

Entry 3 – Level 1

Name: ....

On this sheet you should assess how you feel about the skills you've been using.
Tick the box that is the closest match to your confidence level for each skill when you complete each unit.

☹ *I need help with this*   ☺ *I'm fairly confident*   ☺ *I'm very confident*

Set a target that you need to work on in the next unit.

Unit 1 Phones

☹ ☺ ☺

A Selecting a phone
I know the maths to use in a question.
☐ ☐ ☐

B Selecting the best deal
I show my working clearly and check my results.
☐ ☐ ☐

C Using the new phones
I explain my answers clearly.
☐ ☐ ☐

D Costs
I can work out the information to use from tables.
☐ ☐ ☐

Things I enjoyed about this unit:

Things I need to work on:

Unit 2 Cycling

☹ ☺ ☺

A Learning the skills
I decide the maths I need to use to work out
my answers.
☐ ☐ ☐

B Buying a bike
I show my working clearly and check my results.
☐ ☐ ☐

C Cycle maintenance
I try different ways to solve a problem.
☐ ☐ ☐

D Training for the Olympics?
I can explain my answers clearly.
☐ ☐ ☐

Things I enjoyed about this unit:

Things I need to work on:

Unit 3 Hazelnut School

☹ ☺ ☺

A Designing the recreation area
I decide the maths I need to use to work out
my answers.
☐ ☐ ☐

B Growing vegetables
I show my working clearly and check my results.
☐ ☐ ☐

C Planning a water feature
I can understand and use information from diagrams.
☐ ☐ ☐

D Designing an activity area
I try different ways to solve a problem.
☐ ☐ ☐

Things I enjoyed about this unit:

Things I need to work on:

Unit 4 Youth Club

☹ 😐 ☺

A Going to the youth club
I explain my answers clearly.
☐ ☐ ☐

B Preparing for the weekend away
I try different ways to solve a problem.
☐ ☐ ☐

C Running the youth club
I decide the maths I need to use to work out
my answers.
☐ ☐ ☐

D Stocking up
I show my working clearly and check my results.
☐ ☐ ☐

Things I enjoyed about this unit:

Things I need to work on:

Unit 5 Walking trip

☹ 😐 ☺

A Train times and fares
I begin to organise my work and check my results.
☐ ☐ ☐

B Buying the equipment
I try different approaches and find ways of
overcoming difficulties that arise.
☐ ☐ ☐

C Camping
I review my work and explain my reasoning.
☐ ☐ ☐

D Climbing the peaks
I can select the maths to use in a wider range
of activities.
☐ ☐ ☐

Things I enjoyed about this unit:

Things I need to work on:

Functional Skills Checklist Level 1

By completing the units in this book, you've been practising the skills to help you work towards Level 1.
Tick the box next to the skills where you feel confident.

Representing
I understand practical problems in familiar and unfamiliar contexts and situations, some of
which are non-routine.
☐

I can identify and obtain necessary information to tackle the problem.
☐

I can select mathematics in an organised way to find solutions.
☐

Analysing
I can apply mathematics in an organised way to find solutions to straightforward practical
problems.
☐

I can use appropriate checking procedures at each stage.
☐

Interpreting
I can interpret and communicate solutions to practical problems, drawing simple conclusions
and giving explanations.
☐

Functional skills self assessment

Level 1

Name: ....

On this sheet you should assess how you feel about the skills you've been using.
Tick the box that is the closest match to your confidence level for each skill when you complete each unit.

☹ *I need help with this*   ☺ *I'm fairly confident*   ☺ *I'm very confident*

Set a target that you need to work on in the next unit.

Unit 1 Holidaying in Florida

A Planning a package
I can use maths skills to solve problems in real situations.

B Orlando weather
I can write explanations and answers that are clear and easy to follow.

C Changing currency
I can write explanations and answers that are clear and easy to follow.

D Scream Towers
I can work out a way to answer a problem in a real context.

Things I enjoyed about this unit:

Things I need to work on:

Unit 2 Smashing Smoothies

A Re-writing recipes
I try to work out a problem using my own ideas.

B The price is right
I use maths skills to solve problems in real situations.

C Units and measuring
I try to work out a problem using my own ideas.

D Which smoothie is best?
I can write explanations and answers that are clear and easy to follow.

Things I enjoyed about this unit:

Things I need to work on:

Unit 3 At the match

A Groundsman
I can work out a way to answer a problem in a real context.

B The fan
I use maths skills to solve problems in real situations.

C Kiosk manager
I can write explanations and answers that are clear and easy to follow.

D Team manager
I try to work out a problem using my own ideas.

Things I enjoyed about this unit:

Things I need to work on:

Unit 4 Catering

☹ 😐 ☺

A Market research
I can write explanations and answers that are clear and easy to follow.

☐ ☐ ☐

B The company premises
I can work out a way to answer a problem in a real context.

☐ ☐ ☐

C Food and nutrition
I use maths skills to solve problems in real situations.

☐ ☐ ☐

D Public image of the company
I try to work out a problem using my own ideas.

☐ ☐ ☐

Things I enjoyed about this unit:

Things I need to work on:

Unit 5 Bedroom makeover

☹ 😐 ☺

A Choosing furniture
I use maths skills to solve problems in real situations.

☐ ☐ ☐

B Fitting in furniture
I try to work out a problem using my own ideas.

☐ ☐ ☐

C Painting and decorating
I use maths skills to solve problems in real situations.

☐ ☐ ☐

D Designing pictures
I can write explanations and answers that are clear and easy to follow.

☐ ☐ ☐

Things I enjoyed about this unit:

Things I need to work on:

Functional Skills Checklist Level 1

By completing the units in this book, you've been practising the skills to help you work towards Level 1. Tick the box next to the skills where you feel confident.

Representing
I understand practical problems in familiar and unfamiliar contexts and situations, some of which are non-routine. ☐

I can identify and obtain necessary information to tackle the problem. ☐

I can select mathematics in an organised way to find solutions. ☐

Analysing
I can apply mathematics in an organised way to find solutions to straightforward practical problems. ☐

I can use appropriate checking procedures at each stage. ☐

Interpreting
I can interpret and communicate solutions to practical problems, drawing simple conclusions and giving explanations. ☐

Functional skills self assessment

Level 1 – Level 2

Name: ....

On this sheet you should assess how you feel about the skills you've been using.
Tick the box that is the closest match to your confidence level for each skill when you complete each unit.

☹ *I need help with this*   😐 *I'm fairly confident*   ☺ *I'm very confident*

Set a target that you need to work on in the next unit.

Unit 1 Post Office

		☹	😐	☺
A	**Preparing for school** I can write answers in a clear and organised way.	☐	☐	☐
B	**Passport** I can work out a way to answer a problem set in a real context.	☐	☐	☐
C	**Post** I can work out which information is relevant and use it to solve a problem that has a number of stages.	☐	☐	☐
D	**Deliveries** I can check results to see if they make sense in the question context.	☐	☐	☐

Things I enjoyed about this unit:

Things I need to work on:

Unit 2 Spheres Ltd

		☹	😐	☺
A	**Making footballs** I try to work out a problem using my own ideas.	☐	☐	☐
B	**Tennis balls** I can work out a way to answer a problem set in a real context.	☐	☐	☐
C	**Packing** I can use my answers to pick the best solution to a problem explaining my thinking.	☐	☐	☐
D	**Sales** I can check results to see if they make sense in the question context.	☐	☐	☐

Things I enjoyed about this unit:

Things I need to work on:

Unit 3 Sorcerer's Battle

		☹	😐	☺
A	**Game on** I can work out a way to answer a problem in a real context.	☐	☐	☐
B	**What's the score?** I can write answers in a clear and organised way.	☐	☐	☐
C	**Stormy Skies** I can work out which information is relevant and use it to solve a problem that has a number of stages.	☐	☐	☐
D	**Online challenge** I can use my answers to pick the best solution to a problem, explaining my thinking.	☐	☐	☐

Things I enjoyed about this unit:

Things I need to work on:

Unit 4 In the water

☹ 😐 ☺

A Swimming pool
I can work out which information is relevant and use it to solve a problem that has a number of stages.
☐ ☐ ☐

B Weather permitting
I can show my method by using maths to write out the answer to the problem.
☐ ☐ ☐

C Scuba diving
I can pick out the information I need from text and use it to solve a problem.
☐ ☐ ☐

D Dive holiday
I can use my answers to pick the best solution to a problem, explaining my thinking.
☐ ☐ ☐

Things I enjoyed about this unit:

Things I need to work on:

Unit 5 Flatbridge School

☹ 😐 ☺

A About the school
I can work out which information is relevant and use it to solve a problem that has a number of stages.
☐ ☐ ☐

B How many students?
I can check results to see if they make sense in the question context.
☐ ☐ ☐

C The new block
I can show my method by using maths to write out the answer to the problem.
☐ ☐ ☐

D The computer room
I can make sense of my answer by writing it in an appropriate format.
☐ ☐ ☐

Things I enjoyed about this unit:

Things I need to work on:

Functional Skills Checklist Level 2

By completing the units in this book, you've been practising the skills to help you work towards Level 2. Tick the box next to the skills where you feel confident.

Representing
I understand routine and non-routine problems in familiar and unfamiliar contexts and situations. ☐

I can identify the situation or problems and the mathematical methods needed to solve them. ☐

I can select a range of mathematics to find solutions. ☐

Analysing
I can apply a range of mathematics to find solutions. ☐

I can use appropriate checking procedures and evaluate their effectiveness at each stage. ☐

Interpreting
I can interpret and communicate solutions to multistage practical problems in familiar and unfamiliar contexts and situations. ☐

I can draw conclusions and provide mathematical justifications. ☐

Functional skills self assessment

Level 2

Name: ....

On this sheet you should assess how you feel about the skills you've been using.
Tick the box that is the closest match to your confidence level for each skill when you complete each unit.

☹ *I need help with this*   😐 *I'm fairly confident*   ☺ *I'm very confident*

Set a target that you need to work on in the next unit.

Unit 1 City break

A Before you go
I can work out what information to use from a variety of different sources.

☹ ☐ 😐 ☐ ☺ ☐

B Getting there
I can use my answers to pick the best solution to a problem and explain my thinking.

☹ ☐ 😐 ☐ ☺ ☐

C Where to stay?
I can work out which information is relevant and use it to solve a problem that has a number of stages.

☹ ☐ 😐 ☐ ☺ ☐

D Vicki's new kilt
I can make sense of my answer by writing it in an appropriate format.

☹ ☐ 😐 ☐ ☺ ☐

Things I enjoyed about this unit:

Things I need to work on:

Unit 2 Managing the supermarket

A Number of sales
I can work out what information to use from a variety of different sources.

☹ ☐ 😐 ☐ ☺ ☐

B The bakery
I can check results to see if they make sense in the question context.

☹ ☐ 😐 ☐ ☺ ☐

C Displaying the bakery products
I can use my answers to pick the best solution to a problem, explaining my thinking.

☹ ☐ 😐 ☐ ☺ ☐

D Expected profit
I can explain my answer in the clearest way possible so it is easy to follow.

☹ ☐ 😐 ☐ ☺ ☐

Things I enjoyed about this unit:

Things I need to work on:

Unit 3 Festival

A Rainy day?
I can work out which information is relevant and use it to solve a problem that has a number of stages.

☹ ☐ 😐 ☐ ☺ ☐

B The stage
I can check results to see if they make sense in the question context.

☹ ☐ 😐 ☐ ☺ ☐

C Lighting the stage
I can show my method by using maths to write out the answer to the problem.

☹ ☐ 😐 ☐ ☺ ☐

D Festival sales
I can solve a problem by breaking it into smaller parts.

☹ ☐ 😐 ☐ ☺ ☐

Things I enjoyed about this unit:

Things I need to work on:

Unit 4 Finance for living

☹ ☺ ☺

A Leaving school
I can work out which information is relevant and use it to solve a problem that has a number of stages.

B Gap year
I can work out what information to use from a variety of different sources.

C University
I can check results to see if they make sense in the question context.

D Where to live?
I can explain my answer in the clearest way possible so it is easy to follow.

Things I enjoyed about this unit:

Things I need to work on:

Unit 5 Building a conservatory

☹ ☺ ☺

A Design
I can show my method by using maths to write out the answer to the problem.

B What materials will be needed?
I can pick out the information I need from text and use it to solve a problem.

C Cost of materials
I can make sense of my answer by writing it in an appropriate format.

D Floor design
I can solve a big problem by breaking it into smaller parts.

Things I enjoyed about this unit:

Things I need to work on:

Functional Skills Checklist Level 2

By completing the units in this book, you've been practising the skills to help you work towards Level 2. Tick the box next to the skills where you feel confident.

Representing
I understand routine and non-routine problems in familiar and unfamiliar contexts and situations.

I can identify the situation or problems and the mathematical methods needed to solve them.

I can select a range of mathematics to find solutions.

Analysing
I can apply a range of mathematics to find solutions.

I can use appropriate checking procedures and evaluate their effectiveness at each stage.

Interpreting
I can interpret and communicate solutions to multistage practical problems in familiar and unfamiliar contexts and situations.

I can draw conclusions and provide mathematical justifications.